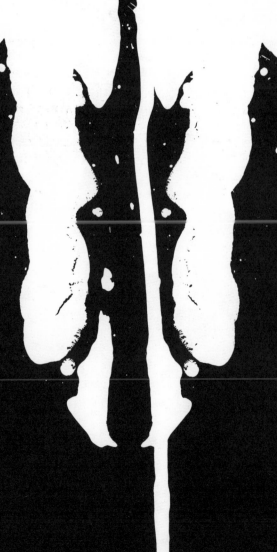

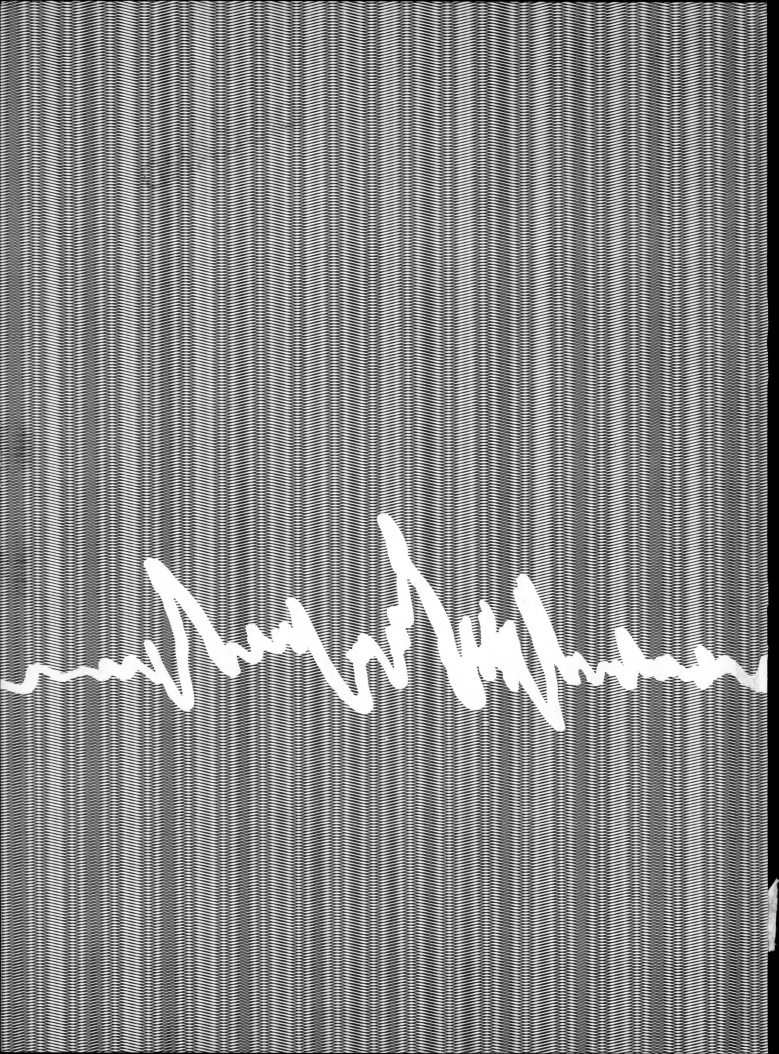

A STRANGE GLORY

EDITED BY GERRY GOLDBERG

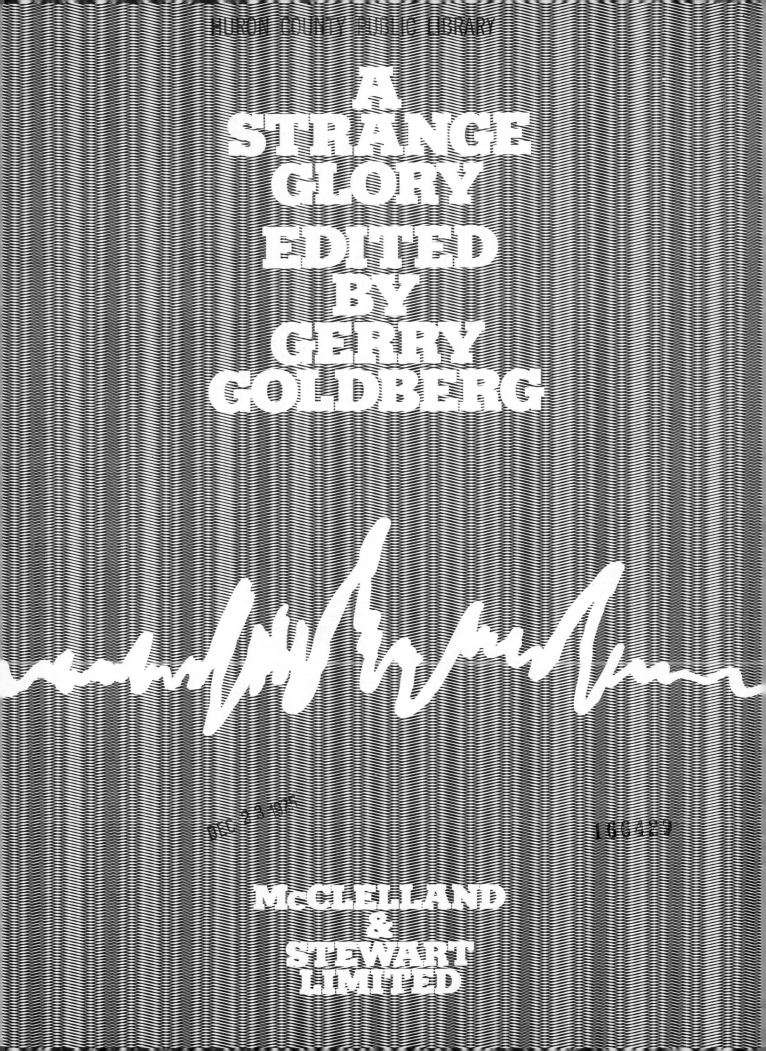

McCLELLAND & STEWART LIMITED

Contents

Copyright © 1975 by McClelland and Stewart Limited

All rights reserved.

The Canadian Publishers
McClelland and Stewart Limited
25 Hollinger Road, Toronto

0-7710-3371-0

Printed and bound in Canada

3. The order disclosed, he longs to be folded in it. But he must not only accept the world—that would be half a life. His imagination and the world are two hands clapping.

4. The sail and the wind that become motion, the sea and the sand that become shore, the universe and the imagination that become man. He is home.

5. Seeing himself, his shape vanishes; dreaming himself, he is real; being most human, he is God.

He too is vulnerable.
He too is exposed.
He too is threatened.
He is bombarded by visions both beautiful and chaotic.
He is deafened by sounds both melodic and discordant.
He has trembled with anxiety.
He has been alienated to the point of turning off.
He has withdrawn from life, hiding himself away.
He has emerged again.
He has thrown back his head to laugh at himself.
He has been shot through with joy.
He has learned to touch and to be touched and to be
   born and reborn in love.
He has brandished his fist in the face of elements both
   natural and man-made which would suck away his
   life and the life of all who live.
He has dared to hope in the face of a sometimes over-
   whelming absurdity.
He has lost, and then gained and lost again; yet each
   time he sensed his own resilience, the positive force
   of his own existence rising up in him.

moments, people and places that gave the book a worth, many thanks to: fred corbett, who gave my dreams meaning, and taught me to see; harlan ellison, who cares so deeply; colin wilson, who began it; gord gemmell, who forced it; the 401, which gave me solitude; may 12, a purpose; keg'n cleaver, may 4, which gave much to enjoy; geny pozzi, who worked so hard; david allen, who listened and david solomon, who had a xerox 4000; jim brotchie, who bothered; jack mcclelland, who had the faith; margaret kent, who lent me her chair and typewriter; diane takerer, who questions; linda mcknight, who believes always; david john shaw, who felt; laura dickson, who smiles; the y.m.h.a., which gave me a place to relax and think; stephen storoschuk, who loves lovecraft; george wright, who scared me; clayton b. ashley, rene, emma, bob and jim, who have that "strange glory"; joan laird, who always reminds me; john colicos, who gave me a choice and introduced me to rye on the rocks; robert "paul" godfrey, who gave my wife so much; duke roberts, who gave me at 4:17 under the bayview bridge my vision; the late jim croce, who gave me "time in a bottle"; mcdonald's and saturdays, which give me precious moments: my mother, who tries constantly; my brothers, who give and give; my father, who taught me to grasp beyond my reach; my wife, who taught me about things that really matter; my daughter sari, who taught me to be........

g.g., 1975

to sari with envy, dreams, and joy

Searching for the Ox

The beast has never gone astray, and what is the use of searching for him?
The reason why the oxherd is not on intimate terms with him is
because the oxherd himself has violated his own inmost nature. The beast is lost,
for the oxherd has himself been led out of the way through his
deluding senses. Desire for gain and fear of loss burn like fire; ideas of right and wrong
shoot up like a phalanx. Alone in the wilderness, lost in the jungle,
the boy is searching, searching! Exhausted and in despair,
he knows not where to go.

The Black Peak
William Wordsworth

One summer evening . . . I found
A little boat tied to a willow-tree
Within a rocky cave, its usual home.
Straight I unloosed her chain, and stepping in
Pushed from the shore. It was an act of stealth
And troubled pleasure, nor without the voice
Of mountain echoes did my boat move on;
Leaving behind her still, on either side,
Small circles glittering idly in the moon,
Until they melted all into one track
Of sparkling light. But now, like one who rows,
Proud of his skill, to reach a chosen point
With an unswerving line, I fixed my view
Upon the summit of a craggy ridge,
The horizon's utmost boundary; far above
Was nothing but the stars and the grey sky.
She was an elfin pinnace; lustily
I dipped my oars into the silent lake,
And, as I rose upon the stroke, my boat
Went heaving through the water like a swan;
When, from behind that craggy steep till then
The horizon's bound, a huge peak, black and huge,
As if with voluntary power instinct
Upreared its head. I struck and struck again,
And growing still in stature the grim shape
Towered up between me and the stars, and still,
For so it seemed, with purpose of its own
And measured motion like a living thing,
Strode after me. With trembling oars I turned,
And through the silent water stole my way
Back to the covert of the willow-tree;
There in her mooring-place I left my bark,
And through the meadows homeward went, in grave
And serious mood; but after I had seen
That spectacle, for many days, my brain
Worked with a dim and undetermined sense
Of unknown modes of being; o'er my thoughts
There hung a darkness, call it solitude
Or blank desertion. No familiar shapes
Remained, no pleasant images of trees,
Of sea or sky, no colours of green fields;
But huge and mighty forms, that do not live
Like living men, moved slowly through the mind
By day, and were a trouble to my dreams.

Midnight
Archibald Lampman

From where I sit, I see the stars,
    And down the chilly floor
The moon between the frozen bars
    Is glimmering dim and hoar.

Without in many a peaked mound
    The glinting snowdrifts lie;
There is no voice or living sound;
    The embers slowly die.

Yet some wild thing is in mine ear;
    I hold my breath and hark;
Out of the depth I seem to hear
    A crying in the dark;

No sound of man or wife or child,
    No sound of beast that groans,
Or of the wind that whistles wild,
    Or of the tree that moans:

I know not what it is I hear;
    I bend my head and hark:
I cannot drive it from mine ear,
    That crying in the dark.

It would be the final error of reason—the point at which it succumbs to its own *hubris* and passes over into its demoniacal opposite, unreason—to deny that the furies exist, or to strive to manipulate them out of existence. Nothing can be accomplished by denying that man is an essentially troubled being, except to make more trouble. We may, of course be able to buy off the Furies for a while; being of the earth and ancient, they have been around much longer than the rational consciousness that would entirely supplant them, and so they can afford to wait. . . . in giving the Furies their place, we may come to recognize that they are not such alien presences as we think in our moments of evading them. In fact, far from being alien, they are part of ourselves, like all gods and demons. The conspiracy to forget them, or to deny that they exist, thus turns out to be only one more contrivance in that vast and organized effort by modern society to flee from the self.

William Barrett, *Irrational Man*

Minotaur
Michael Ayrton

What is a man that I am not a man
Sitting cramped pupate in this chrysalis?
My tongue is gagged with cud and lolls round words
To speak impeded of my legend death.
My horns lack weapon purpose, cannot kill
And cannot stab the curtain of the dark.

Appear, appear, what so thy shape or name,
O Mountain Bull, Snake of the Hundred Heads,
Lion of the Burning Flame!
O God, Beast, Mystery, come!

Euripides

Our ordinary assumptions about the nature of the world
are generally useful to us. As we attempt to achieve a
stable consciousness, we continuously "bet" about the
nature of reality. We immediately assume that our rooms
are "really" rectilinear, that a piece of coal is "really"
black, that one person is intelligent, another aggressive.
. . . our assumptive world is conservative. It is quite difficult for us to alter our assumptions even in the face of
compelling new evidence. We pay the price of a certain
conservatism and resistance to new input in order to
gain a measure of stability in our personal consciousness.

Robert Ornstein, *The Psychology of Consciousness*

The Trap
Jon Stallworthy

The first night that the monster lurched
Out of the forest on all fours,
He saw its shadow in his dream
Circle the house, as though it searched
For one it loved or hated. Claws
On gravel and a rabbit's scream
Ripped the fabric of his dream.

Waking between dark and dawn
And sodden sheets, his reason quelled
The shadow and the nightmare sound.
The second night it crossed the lawn
A brute voice in the darkness yelled.
He struggled up, woke raving, found
His wall-flowers trampled to the ground.

When rook wings beckoned the shadows back
He took his rifle down, and stood
All night against the leaded glass.
The moon ticked round. He saw the black
Elm-skeletons in the doomsday wood,
The sailing and the failing stars
And red coals dropping between bars.

The third night such a putrid breath
Fouled, flared his nostrils, that he turned,
Turned, but could not lift, his head.
A coverlet as thick as death
Oppressed him: he crawled out: discerned
Across the door his watchdog, dead.
"Build a trap," the neighbours said.

All that day he built his trap
With metal jaws and a spring as thick
As the neck of a man. One touch
Triggered the hanging teeth: jump, snap,
And lightning guillotined the stick
Thrust in its throat. With gun and torch
He set his engine in the porch.

The fourth night in their beds appalled
His neighbours heard the hunting roar
Mount, mount to an exultant shriek.
At daybreak timidly they called
His name, climbed through the splintered door
And found him sprawling in the wreck,
Naked, with a severed neck.

The Fear
Andrew Young

How often I turn round
To face the beast that bound by bound
Leaps on me from behind,
Only to see a bough that heaves
With sudden gust of wind
Or blackbird raking withered leaves

A dog may find me out
Or badger toss a white-lined snout;
And one day as I softly trod
Looking for nothing stranger than
A fox or stoat I met a man
And even that seemed not too odd.

And yet in any place I go
I watch and listen as all creatures do
For what I cannot see or hear,
For something warns me everywhere
That even in my land of birth
I trespass on the earth.

The Theogony
Hesiod,
Translated by C.A. Elton

Embraced by Saturn, Rhea gave to light
A glorious race . . .
But then, as issuing from the sacred womb
They touch'd the mother's knees, did Saturn huge
Devour, revolving in his troubled thought
Lest other of celestials should possess
Amidst th'immortals kingly sway, for he
Had heard from Earth and from the starry Heaven
That it was doom'd by Fate, strong though he were,
To his own son he should bow down his strength.
Jove's wisdom this fulfill'd. No blind design
He therefore cherish'd and in crooked craft
Devour'd his children. But on Rhea prey'd
Never-forgotten anguish . . .

We are betrayed by what is false within.

George Meredith

If the only tool you have is a hammer, you tend to treat everything as if it were a nail.

Abraham Maslow, *The Psychology of Science: a Reconnaissance*

The Dweller in Dark Valley
Robert E. Howard

The nightwinds tossed the tangled trees, the stars were cold with scorn;
Midnight lay over Dark Valley the hour I was born.
The mid-wife dozed beside the hearth, a hand the window tried—
She woke and stared and screamed and swooned at what she saw outside.

Her hair was white as a leper's hand, she never spoke again;
But laughed and wove the wild flowers into an endless chain.
But when my childish tongue could speak, and my infant feet could stray,
I found her dying in the hills at the haunted dusk of day.

And her darkening eyes at last were sane; she passed with a fearsome word:
"You who were born in Dark Valley, beware the Valley's lord!"
As I came down through Dark Valley, the grim hills gulped the light;
I heard the ponderous tramping of a monster in the night.

The great trees leaned together, the vines ensnared my feet,
I heard across the darkness my own heart's thundering beat.
Damned be the dark ends of the earth where old horrors live again.
And monsters of lost ages lurk to eat the souls of men!

I climbed the ridge into the moon and trembling there I turned—
Down in the blasted shadows two eyes like hellfire burned.
Under the black malignant trees a shapeless Shadow fell—
I go no more to Dark Valley which is the Gate of Hell.

The outer divorced from any illumination from the inner
is a state of darkness. We are in an age of darkness.

R.D. Laing, *The Politics of Experience*

The Mental Traveller
William Blake

I travel'd thro' a Land of Men,
A Land of Men & Women too,
And heard & saw such dreadful things
As cold Earth wanderers never knew.

For there the Babe is born in joy
That was begotten in dire woe;
Just as we Reap in joy the fruit
Which we in bitter tears did sow.

And if the Babe is born a Boy
He's given to a Woman Old,
Who nails him down upon a rock,
Catches his shrieks in cups of gold.

She binds iron thorns around his head,
She pierces both his hands & feet,
She cuts his heart out at his side
To make it feel both cold & heat.

Her fingers number every Nerve,
Just as a Miser counts his gold;
She lives upon his shrieks & cries,
And she grows young as he grows old.

Till he becomes a bleeding youth,
And she becomes a Virgin bright;
Then he rends up his Manacles
And binds her down for his delight.

He plants himself in all her Nerves,
Just as a Husbandman his mould;
And she becomes his dwelling place
And Garden fruitful seventy fold.

An aged Shadow, soon he fades,
Wand'ring round an Earthly Cot,
Full filled all with gems & gold
Which he by industry had got.

And these are the gems of the Human Soul,
The rubies & pearls of a lovesick eye,
The countless gold of the akeing heart,
The martyr's groan & the lover's sigh.

They are his meat, they are his drink;
He feeds the Beggar & the Poor
And the wayfaring Traveller:
For ever open is his door.

His grief is their eternal joy;
They make the roofs & walls to ring;
Till from the fire on the hearth
A little Female Babe does spring.

And she is all of solid fire
And gems & gold, that none his hand
Dares stretch to touch her Baby form,
Or wrap her in his swaddling-band.

But She comes to the Man she loves,
If young or old, or rich or poor;
They soon drive out the aged Host,
A Beggar at another's door.

He wanders weeping far away,
Until some other take him in;
Oft blind & age-bent, sore distrest,
Untill he can a Maiden win.

And to allay his freezing Age
The Poor Man takes her in his arms;
The Cottage fades before his sight,
The Garden & its lovely Charms.

The Guests are scatter'd thro' the land,
For the Eye altering alters all;
The Senses roll themselves in fear,
And the flat Earth becomes a Ball;

The stars, sun, Moon, all shrink away,
A desart vast without a bound,
And nothing left to eat or drink,
And a dark desart all around.

The honey of her Infant lips,
The bread & wine of her sweet smile,
The wild game of her roving Eye,
Does him to Infancy beguile;

For as he eats & drinks he grows
Younger & younger every day;
And on the desart wild they both
Wander in terror & dismay.

Like the wild Stag she flees away,
Her fear plants many a thicket wild;
While he pursues her night & day,
By various arts of Love beguil'd,

By various arts of Love & Hate,
Till the wide desart planted o'er
With Labyrinths of wayward Love,
Where roam the Lion, Wolf & Boar,

Till he becomes a wayward Babe,
And she a weeping Woman Old.
Then many a Lover wanders here;
The Sun & Stars are nearer roll'd.

The trees bring forth sweet Extacy
To all who in the desart roam;
Till many a City there is Built,
And many a pleasant Shepherd's home.

But when they find the frowning Babe,
Terror strikes thro' the region wide:
They cry "The Babe! the Babe is Born!"
And flee away on Every side.

For who dare touch the frowning form,
His arm is wither'd to its root;
Lions, Boars, Wolves, all howling flee,
And every Tree does shed its fruit.

And none can touch that frowning form,
Except it be a Woman Old;
She nails him down upon the Rock,
And all is done as I have told.

The Magi
W.B. Yeats

Now as at all times I can see in the mind's eye,
In their stiff, painted clothes, the pale unsatisfied ones
Appear and disappear in the blue depth of the sky
With all their ancient faces like rain-beaten stones,
And all their helms of silver hovering side by side,
And all their eyes still fixed, hoping to find once more,
Being by Calvary's turbulence unsatisfied,
The uncontrollable mystery on the bestial floor.

People who have lost the sense of their identity as selves also tend to lose their sense of relatedness to nature. They lose not only their experience of organic connection with inanimate nature, such as trees and mountains, but they also lose some of their capacity to feel empathy for animate nature, that is animals . . .

Our relation to nature tends to be destroyed not only by our emptiness, but also by our anxiety.

Rollo May, *Man's Search for Himself*

The Kraken
Alfred, Lord Tennyson

Below the thunders of the upper deep,
Far, far beneath in the absymal sea,
His ancient, dreamless, uninvaded sleep
The Kraken sleepeth: faintest sunlights flee
About his shadowy sides; above him swell
Huge sponges of milennial growth and height;
And far away into the sickly light,
From many a wondrous grot and secret cell
Unnumber'd and enormous polypi
Winnow with giant arms the slumbering green.
There hath he lain for ages, and will lie
Battening upon huge sea-worms in his sleep,
Until the latter fire shall heat the deep;
Then once by man and angels to be seen,
In roaring he shall rise and on the surface die.

With the supreme power or that sovereign cause which pervades everything, taking new forms according to its surroundings, yet never seen in final shape. The dragon is the great mystery itself. Hidden in the caverns of inaccessible mountains, or coiled in the unfathomed depths of the sea, he awaits the time when he slowly rouses himself to activity. He unfolds himself in the storm clouds; he washes his mane in the blackness of the seething whirlpools. His claws are in the forks of the lightning, his scales begin to glisten in the bark of rain-swept pine trees. His voice is heard in the hurricane which, scattering the withered leaves of the forest, quickens the new spring. The dragon reveals himself only to vanish.

Okakura Kakuzo

The Outsider

H.P. Lovecraft

That night the Baron dreamt of many a wo;
And all his warrior-guests, with shade and form
Of witch, and demon, and large coffin-worm,
Were long be-nightmared–Keats.

Unhappy is he to whom the memories of childhood bring only fear and sadness. Wretched is he who looks back upon lone hours in vast and dismal chambers with brown hangings and maddening rows of antique books, or upon awed watches in twilight groves of grotesque, gigantic, and vine-encumbered trees that silently wave twisted branches far aloft. Such a lot the gods gave to me—to me, the dazed, the disappointed; the barren, the broken. And yet I am strangely content and cling desperately to those sere memories, when my mind momentarily threatens to reach beyond to *the other*.

I know not where I was born, save that the castle was infinitely old and infinitely horrible, full of dark passages and having high ceilings where the eye could find only cobwebs and shadows. The stones in the crumbling corridors seemed always hideously damp, and there was an accursed smell everywhere, as of the piled-up corpses of dead generations. It was never light, so that I used sometimes to light candles and gaze steadily at them for relief, nor was there any sun outdoors, since the terrible trees grew high above the topmost accessible tower. There was one black tower which reached above the trees into the unknown outer sky, but that was partly ruined and could not be ascended save by a well-nigh impossible climb up the sheer wall, stone by stone.

I must have lived years in this place, but I cannot measure the time. Beings must have cared for my needs, yet I cannot recall any person except myself, or anything alive but the noiseless rats and bats and spiders. I think that whoever nursed me must have been shockingly aged, since my first conception of a living person was that of somebody mockingly like myself, yet distorted, shrivelled, and decaying like the castle. To me there was nothing grotesque in the bones and skeletons that strewed some of the stone crypts deep down among the foundations. I fantastically associated these things with everyday events, and thought them more natural than the coloured pictures of living beings which I found in many of the mouldy books. From such books I learned all that I know. No teacher urged or guided me, and I do not recall hearing any human voice in all those years—not even my own; for although I had read of speech, I had never thought to try to speak aloud. My aspect was a matter equally unthought of, for there were no mirrors in the castle, and I merely regarded myself by instinct as akin to the youthful figures I saw drawn and painted in the books. I felt conscious of youth because I remembered so little.

Outside, across the putrid moat and under the

dark mute trees, I would often lie and dream for hours about what I read in the books; and would longingly picture myself amidst gay crowds in the sunny world beyond the endless forests. Once I tried to escape from the forest, but as I went farther from the castle the shade grew denser and the air more filled with brooding fear; so that I ran frantically back lest I lose my way in a labyrinth of nighted silence.

So through endless twilights I dreamed and waited, though I knew not what I waited for. Then in the shadowy solitude my longing for light grew so frantic that I could rest no more, and I lifted entreating hands to the single black ruined tower that reached above the forest into the unknown outer sky. And at last I resolved to scale that tower, fall though I might; since it were better to glimpse the sky and perish, than to live without ever beholding day.

In the dank twilight I climbed the worn and aged stone stairs till I reached the level where they ceased, and thereafter clung perilously to small footholds leading upward. Ghastly and terrible was that dead, stairless cylinder of rock; black, ruined, and deserted, and sinister with startled bats whose wings made no noise. But more ghastly and terrible still was the slowness of my progress; for climb as I might, the darkness overhead grew no thinner, and a new chill as of haunted and venerable mould assailed me. I shivered as I wondered why I did not reach the light, and would have looked down had I dared. I fancied that night had come suddenly upon me, and vainly groped with one free hand for a window embrasure, that I might peer out and above, and try to judge the height I had attained.

All at once, after an infinity of awesome, sightless, crawling up that concave and desperate precipice, I felt my head touch a solid thing, and knew I must have gained the roof, or at least some kind of floor. In the darkness I raised my free hand and tested the barrier, finding it stone and immovable. Then came a deadly circuit of the tower, clinging to whatever holds the slimy wall could give; till finally my testing hand found the barrier yielding, and I turned upward again, pushing the slab or door with my head as I used both hands in my fearful ascent. There was no light revealed above, and as my hands went higher I knew that my climb was for the nonce ended; since the slab was the trap-door of an aperture leading to a level stone surface of greater circumference than the lower tower, no doubt the floor of some lofty and capacious observation chamber. I crawled through carefully, and tried to prevent the heavy slab from falling back into place, but failed in the latter attempt. As I lay exhausted on the stone floor I heard the eerie echoes of its fall, but hoped when necessary to pry it up again.

Believing I was now at prodigious height, far above the accursed branches of the wood, I dragged myself up from the floor and fumbled about for windows, that I might look for the first time upon the sky, and the moon and stars of which I had read. But on every hand I was disappointed; since all that I found were vast shelves of marble, bearing odious oblong boxes of disturbing size. More and more I reflected, and wondered what hoary secrets might abide in this high apartment so many aeons cut off from the castle below. Then unexpectedly my hands came upon a doorway, where hung a portal of stone, rough with strange chiselling. Trying it, I found it locked; but with a supreme burst of strength I overcame all obstacles and dragged it open inward. As I did so there came to me the purest ecstasy I have ever known; for shining tranquilly through an ornate grating of iron, and down a short stone passageway of steps that ascended from the newly found doorway, was the radiant full moon, which I had never before seen save in dreams and in vague visions I dared not call memories.

Fancying now that I had attained the very pinnacle of the castle, I commenced to rush up the few steps beyond the door; but the sudden veiling of the moon

by a cloud caused me to stumble, and I felt my way more slowly in the dark. It was still very dark when I reached the grating—which I tried carefully and found unlocked, but which I did not open for fear of falling from the amazing height to which I had climbed. Then the moon came out.

Most demoniacal of all shocks is that of the abysmally unexpected and grotesquely unbelievable. Nothing I had before undergone could compare in terror with what I now saw; with the bizarre marvels that sight implied. The sight itself was as simple as it was stupefying, for it was merely this: instead of a dizzying prospect of treetops seen from a lofty eminence, there stretched around me on the level through the grating nothing less than *the solid ground*, decked and diversified by marble slabs and columns, and overshadowed by an ancient stone church, whose ruined spire gleamed spectrally in the moonlight.

Half unconscious, I opened the grating and staggered out upon the white gravel path that stretched away in two directions. My mind, stunned and chaotic as it was, still held the frantic craving for light; and not even the fantastic wonder which had happened could stay my course. I neither knew nor cared whether my experience was insanity, dreaming, or magic; but was determined to gaze on brilliance and gaiety at any cost. I knew not who I was or what I was, or what my surroundings might be; though as I continued to stumble alone I became conscious of a kind of fearsome latent memory that made my progress not wholly fortuitous. I passed under an arch out of that region of slabs and columns, and wandered through the open country; sometimes following the visible road, but sometimes leaving it curiously to tread across meadows where only occasional ruins bespoke the ancient presence of a forgotten road. Once I swam across a swift river where crumbling, mossy masonry told of a bridge long vanished.

Over two hours must have passed before I reached what seemed to be my goal, a venerable ivied castle in a thickly wooded park, maddeningly familiar, yet full of perplexing strangeness to me. I saw that the moat was filled in, and that some of the well-known towers were demolished; whilst new wings existed to confuse the beholder. But what I observed with chief interest and delight were the open windows—gorgeously ablaze with light and sending forth sound of the gayest revelry. Advancing to one of these I looked in and saw an oddly dressed company, indeed; making merry, and speaking brightly to one another. I had never, seemingly, heard human speech before and could guess only vaguely what was said. Some of the faces seemed to hold expressions that brought up

incredibly remote recollections, others were utterly alien.

I now stepped through the low window into the brilliantly lighted room, stepping as I did so from my single bright moment of hope to my blackest convulsion of despair and realization. The nightmare was quick to come, for as I entered, there occurred immediately one of the most terrifying demonstrations I had ever conceived. Scarcely had I crossed the sill when there descended upon the whole company a sudden and unheralded fear of hideous intensity, distorting every face and evoking the most horrible screams from nearly every throat. Flight was univer-

sal, and in the clamour and panic several fell in a swoon and were dragged away by their madly fleeing companions. Many covered their eyes with their hands, and plunged blindly and awkwardly in their race to escape, overturning furniture and stumbling against the walls before they managed to reach one of the many doors.

The cries were shocking; and as I stood in the brilliant apartment alone and dazed, listening to their vanishing echoes, I trembled at the thought of what might be lurking near me unseen. At a casual inspection the room seemed deserted, but when I moved towards one of the alcoves I thought I detected a presence there — a hint of motion beyond the golden-arched doorway leading to another and somewhat similar room. As I approached the arch I began to perceive the presence more clearly; and then, with the first and last sound I ever uttered—a ghastly ululation that revolted me almost as poignantly as its noxious cause—I beheld in full, frightful vividness the inconceivable, indescribable, and unmentionable monstrosity which had by its simple appearance changed a merry company to a herd of delirious fugitives.

I cannot even hint what it was like, for it was a compound of all that is unclean, uncanny, unwelcome, abnormal, and detestable. It was the ghoulish shade of decay, antiquity, and dissolution; the putrid, dripping eidolon of unwholesome revelation, the awful baring of that which the merciful earth should always hide. God knows it was not of this world—or no longer of this world—yet to my horror I saw in its eaten-away and bone-revealing outlines a leering, abhorrent travesty on the human shape; and in its mouldy, disintegrating apparel an unspeakable quality that chilled me even more.

I was almost paralysed, but not too much so to make a feeble effort towards flight; a backward stumble which failed to break the spell in which the nameless, voiceless monster held me. My eyes bewitched by the glassy orbs which stared loathsomely into them, refused to close; though they were mercifully blurred, and showed the terrible object but indistinctly after the first shock. I tried to raise my hand to shut out the sight, yet so stunned were my nerves that my arm could not fully obey my will. The attempt, however, was enough to disturb my balance; so that I had to stagger forward several steps to avoid falling. As I did so I became suddenly and agonizingly aware of the *nearness* of the carrion thing, whose hideous hollow breathing I half fancied I could hear. Nearly mad, I found myself yet able to throw out a hand to ward off the foetid apparition which pressed so close; when in one cataclysmic second of cosmic nightmarishness and hellish accident *my fingers touched the rotting outstretched paw of the monster beneath the golden arch.*

I did not shriek, but all the fiendish ghouls that ride the night-wind shrieked for me as in that same second there crashed down upon my mind a single and fleeting avalanche of soul-annihilating memory. I knew in that second all that had been; I remembered beyond the frightful castle and the trees, and recognized the altered edifice in which I now stood; I recognized, most terrible of all, the unholy abomination that stood leering before me as I withdrew my sullied fingers from its own.

But in the cosmos there is balm as well as bitterness, and that balm is nepenthe. In the supreme horror of that second I forgot what had horrified me, and the burst of black memory vanished in a chaos of echoing images. In a dream I fled from that haunted and accursed pile, and ran swiftly and silently in the moonlight. When I returned to the churchyard place of marble and went down the steps I found the stone trap-door immovable; but I was not sorry, for I had hated the antique castle and the trees. Now I ride with the mocking and friendly ghouls on the night-wind, and play by day amongst the catacombs of Nephren-Ka in the sealed and unknown valley of Hadoth by the Nile. I know that light is not for me, save that of the moon over the rock tombs of Neb, nor any gaiety save the unnamed feasts of Nitokris beneath the Great Pyramid; yet in my new wildness and freedom I almost welcome the bitterness of alienage.

For although nepenthe has calmed me, I know always that I am an outsider; a stranger in this century and among those who are still men. This I have known ever since I stretched out my fingers to the abomination within that great gilded frame; stretched out my fingers and touched *a cold and unyielding surface of polished glass.*

I'm just a collection of mirrors, reflecting what everyone else expects of me.

Rollo May, *Man's Search for Himself*

The City of The End of Things
Archibald Lampman

Beside the pounding cataracts
Of midnight streams unknown to us
'Tis builded in the leaflets tracts
And valleys huge of Tartarus.
Lurid and lofty and vast it seems;
It hath no rounded name that rings,
But I have heard it called in dreams
The City of the End of Things.

Its roofs and iron towers have grown
None knoweth how high within the night,
But in its murky streets far down
A flaming terrible and bright
Shakes all the stalking shadows there,
Across the walls, across the floors,
And shifts upon the upper air
From out a thousand furnace doors;
And all the while an awful sound
Keeps roaring on continually,
And crashes in the ceaseless round
Of a gigantic harmony.
Through its grim depths re-echoing
And all its weary height of walls,
With measured roar and iron ring,
The inhuman music lifts and falls.
Where no thing rests and no man is,
And only fire and night hold sway;
The beat, the thunder, and the hiss
Cease not, and change not, night nor day.
And moving at unheard commands,
The abysses and vast fires between,
Flit figures that with clanking hands
Obey a hideous routine;
They are not flesh, they are not bone,
They see not with the human eye,
And from their iron lips is blown
A dreadful and monotonous cry;
And whoso of our mortal race
Should find that city unaware,
Lean Death would smite him face to face,
And blanch him with its venomed air:
Or caught by the terrific spell,
Each thread of memory snapt and cut,
His soul would shrivel and its shell
Go rattling like an empty nut.

It was not always so, but once,
In days that no man thinks upon,
Fair voices echoed from its stones,
The light above it leaped and shone:
Once there were multitudes of men,
That built that city in their pride,
Until its might was made, and then
They withered age by age and died.
But now of that prodigious race,
Three only in an iron tower,
Set like carved idols face to face,
Remain the masters of its power;
And at the city gate a fourth,
Gigantic and with dreadful eyes,
Sits looking toward the lightless north,
Beyond the reach of memories;
Fast rooted to the lurid floor,
A bulk that never moves a jot,
In his pale body dwells no more,
Or mind or soul,—an idiot!
But sometime in the end those three
Shall perish and their hands be still.
And with the master's touch shall flee
Their incommunicable skill.
A stillness absolute as death
Along the slacking wheels shall lie,
And, flagging at a single breath,
The fires shall moulder out and die.
The roar shall vanish at its height,
And over that tremendous town
The silence of eternal night
Shall gather close and settle down.
All its grim grandeur, tower and hall,
Shall be abandoned utterly,
And into rust and dust shall fall
From century to century;
Nor ever living thing shall grow,
Nor trunk of tree, nor blade of grass;
No drop shall fall, no wind shall blow,
Nor sound of any foot shall pass:
Alone of its accursed state,
One thing the hand of Time shall spare,
For the grim Idiot at the gate
Is deathless and eternal there.

Antichrist as a Child
James Reaney

When Antichrist was a child
He caught himself tracing
The capital letter A
On a window sill
And wondered why
Because his name contained no A.
And as he crookedly stood
In his mother's flower-garden
He wondered why she looked so sadly
Out of an upstairs window at him.
He wondered why his father stared so
Whenever he saw his little son
Walking in his soot-colored suit.
He wondered why the flowers
And even the ugliest weeds
Avoided his fingers and his touch.
And when his shoes began to hurt
Because his feet were becoming hooves
He did not let on to anyone
For fear they would shoot him for a monster.
He wondered why he more and more
Dreamed of eclipses of the sun,
Of sunsets, ruined towns and zeppelins,
And especially inverted, upside down churches.

I am beginning to realize that "sanity" is no longer a value or an end in itself. The "sanity" of modern man is about as useful to him as the huge bulk and muscles of the dinosaur. If he were a little less sane, a little more doubtful, a little more aware of his absurdities and contradictions, perhaps there might be a possibility of his survival. But if he is sane, too sane ... perhaps we must say that in a society like ours the worst insanity is totally without anxiety, totally "sane."

Thomas Merton, *Raids on the Unspeakable*

Paranoid
P.K. Page

He loved himself too much. As a child was god.
Thunder stemmed from his whims,
flowers were his path.
Throughout those early days his mother was all love,
a warm projection of him
like a second heart.

In adolescence, dark and silent, he was perfect;
still godlike and like a god
cast the world out.
Crouching in his own torso as in a chapel
the stained glass of his blood
glowed in the light.

Remained a god. Each year he grew more holy
and more wholly himself.
The self spun
thinner and thinner like a moon forming
slowly from that other self
the dead sun.

Until he was alone, revolved in ether
light years from the world,
cold and remote.
Thinking he owned the heavens too, he circled,
wanly he turned and whirled
reflecting light.

This Is a Clearing
Joy Kogawa

This is a clearing
There is the forest
This is the forest
There is the clearing.
My gentle relatives are standing in dark sunlight
Whispered about with monumental propriety
Gathering on the occasion of a wedding
To impale and dismember a missing relative
Chanting a creed "We belong. We belong."
I stand on the edge
If I enter the forest I am lost
If I enter the clearing I am still lost
I move in a direction
Chanting a creed, "We belong. We belong."
A large tree cracks

We need not be unaware of the "inner" world. We do not realize its existence most of the time. But many people enter it—unfortunately without guides, confusing outer with inner realities, and inner with outer—and generally lose their capacity to function competently in ordinary relations.

R.D. Laing, *The Politics of Experience*

To End her Fear
John Freeman

Be kind to her
O Time.
She is too much afraid of you
    Because yours is a land unknown,
    Wintry, dark and lone.

'Tis not for her
To pass
Boldly upon your roadless waste.
    Roads she loves, and the bright ringing
    Of quick heels, and clear singing.

She is afraid
Of Time,
Forty to seventy sadly fearing . . .
    O, all those unknown years,
    And these sly, stoat-like fears!

Shake not on her
Your snows,
But on the rich, the proud, the wise
    Who have that to make them glow
    With warmth beneath the snow.

If she grow old
At last,
    Be it yet unknown to her; that she
    Not until her last prayer is prayed
    May whisper, "I am afraid!"

all the trees coloured were
Joy Kogawa

all the trees coloured were
bird full and song ready to move
the forests alive with leaf swish and
ballet shoes on when suddenly
the "no" storm fell cloud down
and curtain heavy i
cocoon the dark
                    grope
my fingernails black
the strange—
everywhere the strange
no colours left—

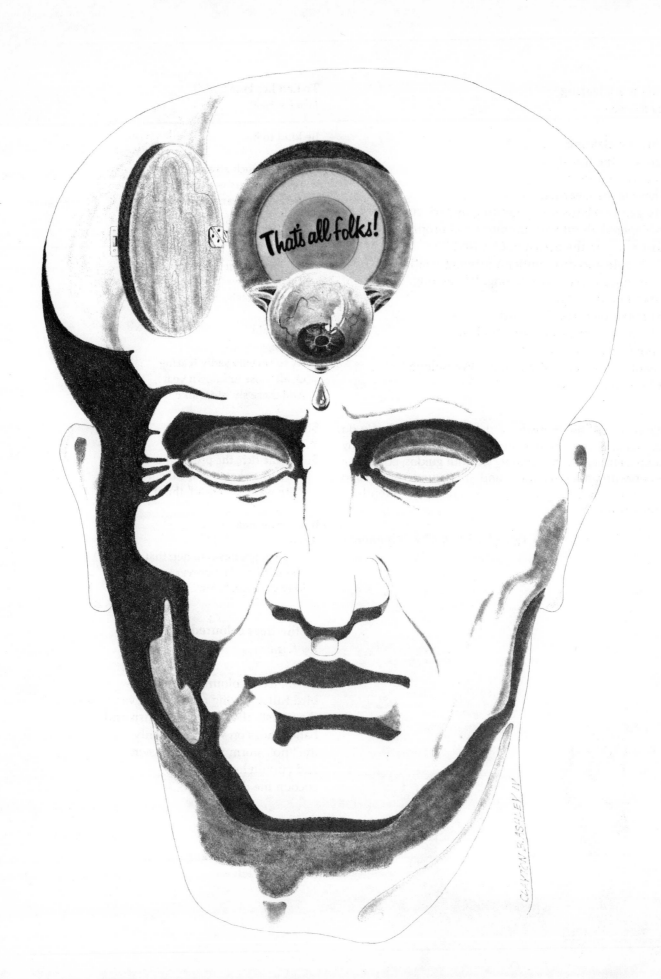

The Door

E.B. White

Everything (he kept saying) is something it isn't. And everybody is always somewhere else. Maybe it was the city, being in the city, that made him feel how queer everything was and that it was something else. Maybe (he kept thinking) it was the names of the things. The names were tex and frequently koid. Or they were flex and oid or they were duroid (sani) or flexsan (duro), but everything was glass (but not quite glass) and the thing that you touched (the surface, washable, crease-resistant) was rubber, only it wasn't quite rubber and you didn't quite touch it but almost. The wall, which was glass but thrutex, turned out on being approached not to be a wall, it was something else, it was an opening or doorway—and the doorway (through which he saw himself approaching) turned out to be something else, it was a wall. And what he had eaten not having agreed with him.

He was in a washable house, but he wasn't sure. Now about those rats, he kept saying to himself. He meant the rats that the Professor had driven crazy by forcing them to deal with problems which were beyond the scope of rats, the insoluble problems. He meant the rats that had been trained to jump at the square card with the circle in the middle, and the card (because it was something it wasn't) would give way and let the rat into a place where the food was, but then one day it would be a trick played on the rat, and the card would be changed, and the rat would jump but the card wouldn't give way, and it was an impossible situation (for a rat) and the rat would go insane and into its eyes would come the unspeakably bright imploring look of the frustrated, and after the convulsions were over and the frantic racing around, then the passive stage would set in and the willingness to let anything be done to it, even if it was something else.

He didn't know which door (or wall) or opening in the house to jump at, to get through, because one was an opening that wasn't an opening, it was a sanitary cupboard of the same color. He caught a glimpse of his eyes staring into his eyes, in the thrutex, and in them was the expression he had seen in the picture of the rats—weary after convulsions and the frantic racing around, when they were willing and did not mind having anything done to them. More and more (he kept saying) I am confronted by a problem which is incapable of solution (for this time even if he chose the right door, there would be no food behind it) and that is what madness is, and things seeming different from what they are. He heard, in the house where he was, in the city to which he had gone (as toward a door which might, or might not, give way), a noise—not a loud noise but more of a low prefabricated humming. It came from a place in the base of the wall (or stat) where the flue carrying the filterable air was, and not far from the Minipiano, which was made of the same material nailbrushes are made of, and which was under the stairs. "This, too, has been tested," she said, pointing, but not at it, "and found viable." It wasn't a loud noise, he kept thinking, sorry that he had seen his eyes, even though it was through his own eyes that he had seen them.

First will come the convulsions (he said), then the exhaustion, then the willingness to let anything be done. "And you better believe it *will* be."

All his life he had been confronted by situations which were incapable of being solved, and there was a deliberateness behind all this, behind this changing of the card (or door), because they would always wait till you had learned to jump at the certain card (or door)—the one with the circle—and then they would change it on you. There have been so many doors changed on me, he said, in the last twenty years, but it is now becoming clear that it is an impossible situation, and the question is whether to jump again, even though they ruffle you in the rump with a blast of air—to make you jump. He wished he wasn't standing by the Minipiano. First they would teach you the prayers and the Psalms, and that would be the right door (the one with the circle), and the long sweet words with the holy sound, and that would be the one to jump at to get where the food was. Then one day you jumped and it didn't give way, so that all you got

was the bump on the nose, and the first bewilderment, the first young bewilderment.

I don't know whether to tell her about the door they substituted or not, he said, the one with the equation on it and the picture of the amoeba reproducing itself by division. Or the one with the photostatic copy of the check for thirty-two dollars and fifty cents. But the jumping was so long ago, although the bump is . . . how those old wounds hurt! Being crazy this way wouldn't be so bad if only, if only. If only when you put your foot forward to take a step, the ground wouldn't come up to meet your foot the way it does. And the same way in the street (only I may never get back to the street unless I jump at the right door), the curb coming up to meet your foot, anticipating ever so delicately the weight of the body, which is somewhere else. "We could take your name," she said, "and send it to you." And it wouldn't be so bad if only you could read a sentence all the way through without jumping (your eye) to something else on the same page; and then (he kept thinking) there was that man out in Jersey, the one who started to chop his trees down, one by one, the man who began talking about how he would take his house to pieces, brick by brick, because he faced a problem incapable of solution, probably, so he began to hack at the trees in the yard, began to pluck with trembling fingers at the bricks in the house. Even if a house is not washable, it is worth taking down. It is not till later that the exhaustion sets in.

But it is inevitable that they will keep changing the doors on you, he said, because that is what they are for; and the thing is to get used to it and not let it unsettle the mind. But that would mean not jumping, and you can't. Nobody can not jump. There will be no not-jumping. Among rats, perhaps, but among people never. Everybody has to keep jumping at a door (the one with the circle on it) because that is the way everybody is, specially some people. You wouldn't want me, standing here, to tell you, would you, about my friend the poet (deceased) who said, "My heart has followed all my days something I cannot name"? (It had the circle on it.) And like many poets, although few so beloved, he is gone. It killed him, the jumping. First, of course, there were the preliminary bouts, the convulsions, and the calm and the willingness.

I remember the door with the picture of the girl on it (only it was spring), her arms outstretched in loveliness, her dress (it was the one with the circle on it) uncaught, beginning the slow, clear, blinding cascade—and I guess we would all like to try that door again, for it seemed like the way and for a while it was the way, the door would open and you would go through winged and exalted (like any rat) and the food would be there, the way the Professor had it arranged, everything O.K., and you had chosen the right door for the world was young. The time they changed that door on me, my nose bled for a hundred hours—how do you like that, Madam? Or would you prefer to show me further through this so strange house, or you could take my name and send it to me, for although my heart has followed all my days something I cannot name, I am tired of the jumping and I do not know which way to go, Madam, and I am not even sure that I am not tried beyond the endurance of man (rat, if you will) and have taken leave of sanity. What are you following these days, old friend, after your recovery from the last bump? What is the name, or is it something you cannot name? The rats have a name for it by this time, perhaps, but I don't know what they call it. I call it plexikoid and it comes in sheets, something like insulating board, unattainable and ugli-proof.

And there was the man out in Jersey, because I keep thinking about his terrible necessity and the passion and trouble he had gone to all those years in the indescribable abundance of a householder's detail, building the estate and the planting of the trees and in spring the lawn-dressing and in fall the bulbs for the spring burgeoning, and the watering of the grass on the long light evenings in summer and the gravel for the driveway (all had to be thought out, planned) and the decorative borders, probably, the perennials and the bug spray, and the building of the house from plans of the architect, first the sills, then the studs, then the full corn in the ear, the floors laid on the floor timbers, smoothed, and then the carpets upon the smooth floors and the curtains and the rods therefor. And then, almost without warning, he would be jumping at the same old door and it wouldn't give: they had changed it on him, making life no longer supportable under the elms in the elm shade, under the maples in the maple shade.

"Here you have the maximum of openness in a small room."

It was impossible to say (maybe it was the city) what made him feel the way he did, and I am not the only one either, he kept thinking—ask any doctor if I am. The doctors, they know how many there are, they even know where the trouble is only they don't like to tell you about the prefrontal lobe because that means making a hole in your skull and removing the work of centuries. It took so long coming, this lobe, so many, many years. (Is it something you read in the paper, perhaps?) And now, the strain being so great, the door having been changed by the Professor once too often . . . but it only means a whiff of ether, a few deft strokes, and the higher animal becomes a little easier in his mind and more like the lower one. From now on, you see, that's the way it will be, the ones with the small prefrontal lobes will win because the other ones are hurt too much by this incessant bumping. They can stand just so much, eh, Doctor? (And what is that, pray, that you have in your hand?) Still, you never can tell, eh, Madam?

He crossed (carefully) the room, the thick carpet under him softly, and went toward the door carefully, which was glass and he could see himself in it, and which, at his approach, opened to allow him to pass through; and beyond he half expected to find one of the old doors that he had known, perhaps the one with the circle, the one with the girl her arms outstretched in loveliness and beauty before him. But he saw instead a moving stairway, and descended in light (he kept thinking) to the street below and to the other people. As he stepped off, the ground came up slightly, to meet his foot.

Whereas man perennially trembles in the face of Paradise Lost—of Chaos, uncertainty, destruction, alienation, night and death—but also of overwhelming ecstasy, life and day, what is of highest concern is the possibility that a heroic vision may dawn within each of us, to be assimilated—beyond theory or intellectualization—into our everyday lives. Only if we gain a sense of integration can we become capable of transfiguring what is narrowly self-serving into what may benefit others. Yet we must ever know that such a phenomenon cannot occur save at the right time, and because of a classic procedure, difficult not merely to describe but, even more important, to endure. The process is impossible to hasten, since it involves both self-discovery and the being transported into harmony with others—as with the very axis of the universe—the most meaningful of all goals.

Dorothy Norman, *The Hero: Myth/Image/Symbol*

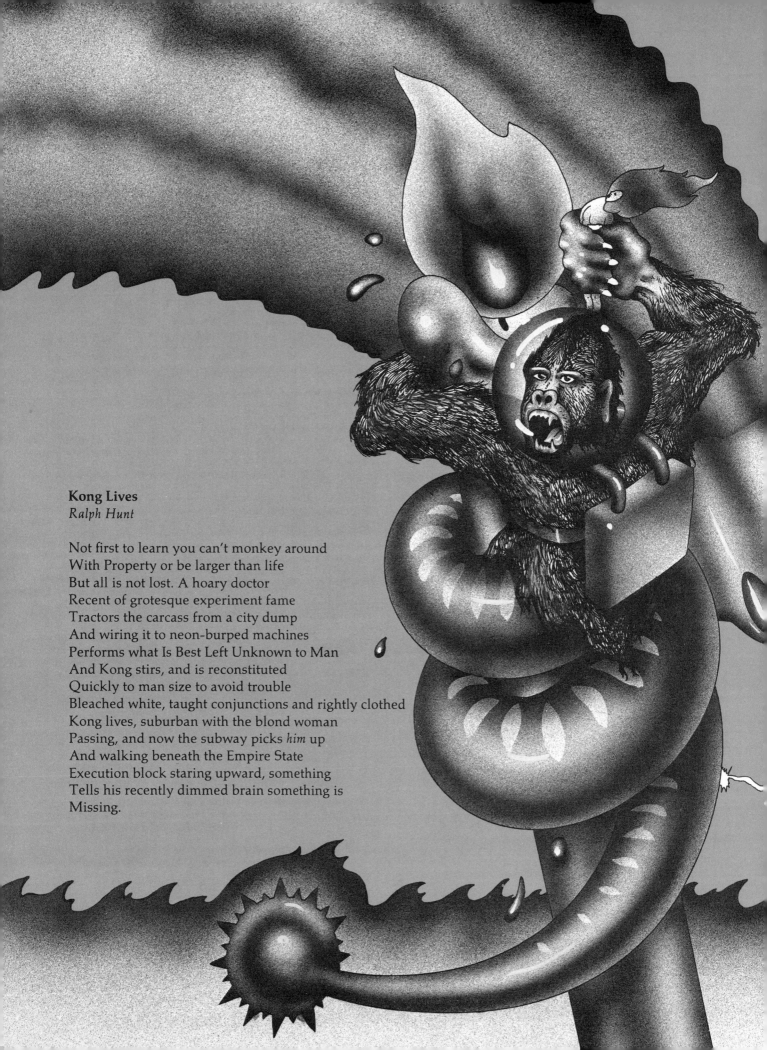

Kong Lives
Ralph Hunt

Not first to learn you can't monkey around
With Property or be larger than life
But all is not lost. A hoary doctor
Recent of grotesque experiment fame
Tractors the carcass from a city dump
And wiring it to neon-burped machines
Performs what Is Best Left Unknown to Man
And Kong stirs, and is reconstituted
Quickly to man size to avoid trouble
Bleached white, taught conjunctions and rightly clothed
Kong lives, suburban with the blond woman
Passing, and now the subway picks *him* up
And walking beneath the Empire State
Execution block staring upward, something
Tells his recently dimmed brain something is
Missing.

Bestiary
A.M. Klein

God breathe a blessing on
His small bones, every one!
The little lad, who stalks
The bible's plains and rocks
To hunt in grammar'd woods
Strange litters and wild broods;
The little lad who seeks
Beast-muzzles and bird-beaks
In cave and den and crypt,
In copse of holy script;
The little lad who looks
For quarry in holy books.

Before his eyes is born
The elusive unicorn;
There, scampering, arrive
The golden mice, the five;
Also, in antic shape,
Gay peacock and glum ape.
He hears a snort of wrath:
The fiery behemoth;
And then on biblic breeze
The crocodile's sneeze.
He sees the lion eat
Straw, and from the teat
Of tigress a young lamb
Suckling, like whelp nigh dam.

Hard by, as fleet as wind
They pass, the roe and hind,
Bravely, and with no risk,
He holds the basilisk,
Pygarg and cockatrice.
And there, most forest-wise
Among the bestiaries
The little hunter eyes
Him crawling at his leisure:
The beast Nebuchadnezzar.

Although he has flourished till now, his relatively brief success on earth has not necessarily promised future survival. For in the long history of life, survival of species has not been the general rule.

The brain is an obstacle in the sense that it is the co-ordinating centre for human movements and appetites. It is necessary to think *in opposition* to the brain.

Gaston Bachelard

Sisters
P.K. Page

These children split each other open like nuts,
break and crack in the small house,
are doors slamming.
Still, on the whole, are gentle for mother, take
her simple comfort like a drink of milk.

Fierce on the street they own the sun and spin
on separate axes
attract about them in their motion all
the shrieking neighborhood of little earths;
in violence hold hatred in their mouths.

With evening their joint gentle laughter leads
them into pastures of each other's eyes;
beyond, the world is barren; they contract
tenderness from each other like disease
and talk as if each word had just been born—
a butterfly, and soft from its cocoon.

Man is an amphibian, Huxley said, living in many worlds at the same time: a world of reason, a world of perception, a world of possible mystical experiences, and several others. But for centuries the education we have received has simply stressed the development of reason and transmission of information, and now many of our other faculties lie dormant or function in aberrant ways.

Claudio Naranjo, *The One Quest*

Dream: Bluejay
or Archeopteryx
Margaret Atwood

kneeling on rock
by lakeside, sun
in the sky and also in
the water, that other
self of mine also
kneeling on rock

on the seared bushes the hard
berries squeezed out from
stem ends in spite of

the red needles crackling
on the ground, the sand, among
the roots, firedry

my four hands gathering
in either world, the berries
in the dish glowed blue
embers

     a bird
lit on both branches

his beak split/his tin
scream forked in the air

warning. above me
against the sun I saw
his lizard eye
          looked
down.   gone

in the water
under my shadow
there was an outline, man
surfacing, his body sheathed
in feathers, his teeth
glinting like nails, fierce god
head crested with blue flame

Most of us have the sensation that "I myself" is a separate center of feeling and action, living inside and bounded by the physical body–a center which "confronts" an "external" world of people and things, making contact through the senses with a universe both alien and strange. Everyday figures of speech reflect this illusion. "I came into this world." "You must face reality." "The conquest of nature."

This feeling of being lonely and very temporary visitors in the universe is in flat contradiction to everything known about man (and all other living organisms) in the sciences. We do not "come into" this world; we come out of it, as leaves from a tree. As the ocean "waves," the universe "peoples." Every individual is an expression of the whole realm of nature, a unique action of the total universe. This fact is rarely, if ever, experienced by most individuals. Even those who know it to be true in theory do not sense or feel it, but continue to be aware of themselves as isolated "egos" inside bags of skin.

The first result of this illusion is that our attitude to the world "outside" us is largely hostile. We are forever "conquering" nature, space, mountains, deserts, bacteria, and insects instead of learning to co-operate with them in a harmonious order.

Alan Watts, *On the Taboo Against Knowing Who You Are*

. . . let us remember that the depth-psychologies have recognised the dimension of the imaginary as one of vital value, as of primordial importance to the human being as a whole. Imaginary experience is constitutive of man, no less certainly than everyday experience and practical activities. Although its structure is not homologous with the structures of "objective" realities, the world of the imaginary is not "unreal".

Mircea Eliade, *Myths, Dreams, and Mysteries*

In a Dark Time
Theodore Roethke

In a dark time, the eye begins to see,
I meet my shadow in the deepening shade;
I hear my echo in the echoing wood—
A lord of nature weeping to a tree.
I live between the heron and the wren,
Beasts of the hill and serpents of the den.

What's madness but nobility of soul
At odds with circumstance? The day's on fire!
I know the purity of pure despair,
My shadow pinned against a sweating wall.
That place among the rocks—is it a cave,
Or winding path? The edge is what I have.

A steady storm of correspondences!
A night flowing with birds, a ragged moon,
And in broad day the midnight come again!
A man goes far to find out what he is—
Death of the self in a long, tearless night,
All natural shapes blazing unnatural light.

Dark, dark my light, and darker my desire.
My soul, like some heat-maddened summer fly,
Keeps buzzing at the sill. Which I is *I*?
A fallen man, I climb out of my fear.
The mind enters itself, and God the mind,
And one is One, free in the tearing wind.

God works by contraries so that a man feels himself to
be lost in the very moment when he is on the point of
being saved. When God is about to justify a man, he
damns him. Whom he would make alive he must first
kill. God's favour is so communicated in the form of
wrath that it seems furthest when it is at hand. Man must
first cry out that there is no health in him. He must be
consumed with horror. This is the pain of purgatory . . .
In this disturbance salvation begins. When a man
believes himself to be utterly lost, light breaks.

Martin Luther

Arras
P.K. Page

Consider a new habit—classical,
and trees espaliered on the wall like candelabra.
How still upon that lawn our sandalled feet.

But a peacock rattling its rattan tail and screaming
has found a point of entry. Through whose eye
did it insinuate in furled disguise
to shake its jewels and silk upon that grass?

The peaches hang like lanterns. No one joins
those figures on the arras.
                              Who am I
or who am I become that walking here
I am observer, other, Gemini,
starred for a green garden of cinema?

I ask, what did they deal me in this pack?
The cards, all suits, are royal when I look.
My fingers slipping on a monarch's face
twitch and go slack.
I want a hand to clutch, a heart to crack.

No one is moving now, the stillness is
infinite. If I should make a break. . . .
take to my springy heels . . . ? But nothing moves.
The spinning world is stuck upon its poles,
the stillness points a bone at me. I fear
the future on this arras.
                              I confess:
It was my eye.
Voluptuous it came.
Its head the ferrule and its lovely tail
folded so sweetly; it was strangely slim
to fit the retina. And then it shook
and was a peacock—living patina,
eye-bright—maculate!
Does no one care?

I thought their hands might hold me if I spoke.
I dreamed the bite of fingers in my flesh,
their poke smashed by an image, but they stand
as if within a treacle, motionless,
folding slow eyes on nothing. While they stare
another line has trolled the encircling air,
another bird assumes its furled disguise.

Growing entails going out of our minds and into our raw experience. Our experience is always of the disclosure of the world and of our own embodied being. When we function smoothly, habitually, and effectively in the world, our concepts are confirmed, and we do not receive new disclosure. When we meet impass and failure in the pursuit of our projects, then our habits and concepts . . . are challenged. Failure of our projects give us a whiff of the stink of chaos, and this can be terrifying. Our concepts get cracks in them when we fail. Through these cracks, the encapsulated experience "contained" by the concept might leak or explode; or through the crack there may occur an implosion of more being. When there are no concepts, there is nothing, no-thing, we can grapple with, get leverage on, in order to get on with the projects of living. There is the threat of pure chaos and nothingness. If we experience the pure nothingness, we panic, and seek quickly to shore up the collapsing world, to daub clay into the cracks of our concepts. If we do this, we don't grow. If we let the concepts explode or implode, and do not re-form them veridically, we appear mad, and are mad. If we re-form them, to incorporate new experience, we grow.

Sidney M. Jourard, "Growing Awareness and the Awareness of Growth" in *Ways of Growth*

Man knows of chaos and creation in the cosmogonic myth and he learns that chaos and creation take place in himself, but he does not see the former and the latter together; he listens to the myth of Lucifer and hushes it up in his own life. He needs the bridge.

Martin Buber

CTHULHU

When the Waters Were Changed
Idries Shah

Once upon a time Khidr, the Teacher of Moses, called upon mankind with a warning. At a certain date, he said, all the water in the world which had not been specially hoarded, would disappear. It would then be renewed, with different water, which would drive men mad.

Only one man listened to the meaning of this advice. He collected water and went to a secure place where he stored it, and waited for the water to change its character.

On the appointed date the streams stopped running, the wells went dry, and the man who had listened, seeing this happening, went to his retreat and drank his preserved water.

When he saw, from his security, the waterfalls again beginning to flow, this man descended among the other sons of men. He found that they were thinking and talking in an entirely different way from before; yet they had no memory of what had happened, nor of having been warned. When he tried to talk to them, he realized that they thought that he was mad, and they showed hostility or compassion, not understanding.

At first he drank none of the new water, but went back to his concealment, to draw on his supplies, every day. Finally, however, he took the decision to drink the new water because he could not bear the loneliness of living, behaving and thinking in a different way from everyone else. He drank the new water, and became like the rest. Then he forgot all about his own store of special water, and his fellows began to look upon him as a madman who had miraculously been restored to sanity.

from On Malay Witchcraft
C.C. Iturvuru

On the stairway of the Tower of Victory there has lived since the beginning of time a being sensitive to the many shades of the human soul and known as the A Bao A Qu. It lies dormant, for the most part on the first step, until at the approach of a person some secret life is touched off in it, and deep within the creature an inner light begins to glow. At the same time, its body and almost translucent skin begin to stir. But only when someone starts up the spiraling stairs is the A Bao A Qu brought to consciousness, and then it sticks close to the visitor's heels, keeping to the outside of the turning steps, where they are most worn by the generations of pilgrims. At each level the creature's color becomes more intense, its shape approaches perfection, and the bluish light it gives off is more brilliant. But it achieves its ultimate form only at the topmost step, when the climber is a person who has attained Nirvana and whose acts cast no shadows. Otherwise, the A Bao A Qu hangs back before reaching the top, as if paralyzed, its body incomplete, its blue growing paler, and its glow hesitant. The creature suffers when it cannot come to completion, and its moan is a barely audible sound, something like the rustling of silk. Its span of life is brief, since as soon as the traveler climbs down, the A Bao A Qu wheels and tumbles to the first steps, where, worn out and almost shapeless, it waits for the next visitor. People say that its tentacles are visible only when it reaches the middle of the staircase. It is also said that it can see with its whole body and that to the touch it is like the skin of a peach.

In the course of the centuries, the A Bao A Qu has reached the terrace only once.

from **A Separate Reality**
Carlos Castaneda

The world is indeed full of frightening things and we are helpless creatures surrounded by forces that are inexplicable and unbending. The average man, in ignorance, believes that those forces can be explained or changed; he doesn't really know how to do that, but he expects that the actions of mankind will explain them or change them sooner or later. The sorcerer, on the other hand, does not think of explaining or changing them; instead, he learns to use such forces by redirecting himself and adapting to their direction. That's his trick. There is very little to sorcery once you find out its trick. A sorcerer is only slightly better off than the average man. Sorcery does not help him to live a better life; in fact I should say that sorcery hinders him; it makes his life cumbersome, precarious. By opening himself to knowledge a sorcerer becomes more vulnerable than the average man. On the one hand his fellow men hate him and fear him and will strive to end his life; on the other hand the inexplicable and unbending forces that surround every one of us, by right of our being alive, are for a sorcerer a source of even greater danger. To be pierced by a fellow man is indeed painful, but nothing in comparison to being touched by an ally. A sorcerer, by opening himself to knowledge falls prey to such forces and has only one means of balancing himself, his will; thus he must feel and act like a warrior. I will repeat this once more: Only as a warrior can one survive the path of knowledge. What helps a sorcerer live a better life is the strength of being a warrior.

Man lives no small part of his life in the presence of the unconscious and the unknown: he is apparently the only creature who ever had the intuition that there is more in nature than meets the eye. In opening up his specific human capacities, the unknown, indeed, the unknowable, has proved an even greater stimulus than the known, while his peculiar fore-consciousness of death has added an enigmatic dimension to his life that has carried him beyond dumb animal acceptance of that terminal event. Infinity, eternity, immortality, potentiality, omniscience, omnipotence, divinity, to say nothing of zero and the square root of minus one, have no counterparts in animal experience.

If the constructive use of dreams differentiates man from other animals, this faculty may have occupied an even greater proportion of early man's attention and interest than overrational interpretations ordinarily allow. In the depths of the human personality, the unconscious and the supernatural are united in the form of dynamic images transcending any actual human experience: demons, monsters, dragons, angels, gods take possession of the dreamer and become more obsessively real than the actual world of here and now, to which he confusedly returns. With these overpowering images, independent and autonomous, sometimes as vivid in daylight as in sleep, man went farther in the direction of detachment and projection: detachment from the animal, projection of the superhuman and the divine.

Lewis Mumford, *The Transformations of Man*

Socrates in Plato's Cave
Stuart Mackinnon

He is a hieroglyph of black stone
much as I have liked to imagine him.
I must say indestructible,
for ignorance is a grey branching root
that creeps off the margin of a decretal
to obscure the figures. His eyes wedge
it and after centuries of confrontation
the walls are cracking by their roots.
At dusk the high gulls catch light
by its slippery wings.

Every individual is at once the beneficiary and the victim of the linguistic tradition into which he or she has been born–the beneficiary inasmuch as language gives access to the accumulated records of other people's experience, the victim in so far as it confirms him in the belief that reduced awareness is the only awareness and as it bedevils his sense of reality, so that he is all too apt to take his concepts for data, his words for actual things. That which, in the language of religion, is called "this world" is the universe of reduced awareness, expressed and, as it were, petrified by language. The various "other worlds," with which human beings erratically make contact are so many elements in the totality of the awareness belonging to Mind at Large.

Aldous Huxley, *The Doors of Perception*

Seeing the Traces

By inquiring into the doctrines, he has come to understand something, he has found
the traces. He now knows that the objective world is a reflection of the Self.
Yet, he is unable to distinguish what is good from what is not,
his mind is still confused as to truth and falsehood. As he has not yet entered
the gate, he is provisionally said to have noticed the traces.

Seeing the Ox

The boy finds the way by the sound he hears; he sees thereby into the origin of things,
and all his senses are in harmonious order. In all his activities,
it is manifestly present. [It is there though not distinguishable as
an individual entity.] When the eye is properly directed, he will find that
it is no other than himself.

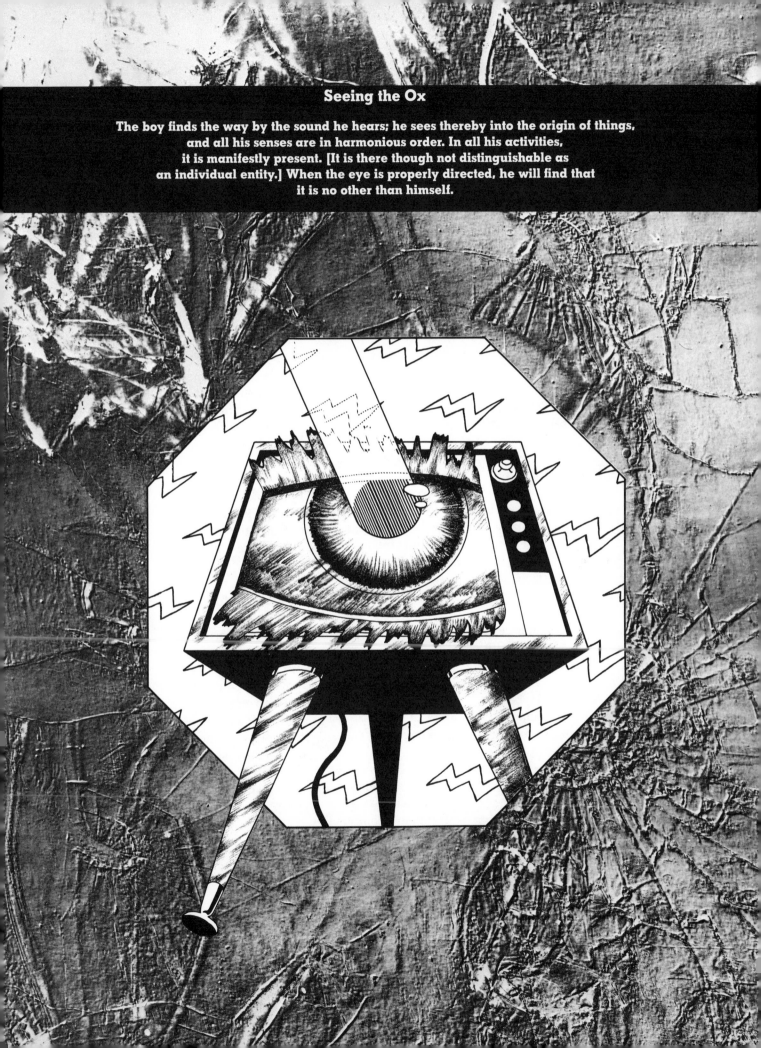

Vancouver Lights
Earle Birney

About me the night   moonless   wimples the mountains
wraps ocean   land   air   and mounting
sucks at the stars   The city   throbbing below
webs the sable peninsula   The golden
strands overleap the seajet   by bridge and buoy
vault the shears of the inlet   climb the woods
toward me   falter   and halt   Across to the firefly
haze of a ship on the gulf's erased horizon
roll the lambent spokes of a lighthouse

Through the feckless years we have come to the time
when to look on this quilt of lamps is a troubling delight
Welling from Europe's bog   through Africa flowing
and Asia   drowning the lonely lumes on the oceans
tiding up over Halifax   now to this winking
outpost comes flooding the primal ink

On this mountain's brutish forehead with terror of space
I stir   of the changeless night and the stark ranges
of nothing   pulsing down from beyond and between
the fragile planets   We are a spark beleaguered
by darkness   this twinkle we make in a corner of emptiness
how shall we utter our fear that the black Experimentress
will never in the range of her microscope find it?   Our Phoebus
himself is a bubble that dries on Her slide   while the Nubian
wears for an evening's whim a necklace of nebulae

Yet we must speak   we the unique glowworms
Out of the waters and rocks of our little world
we conjured these flames   hooped these sparks
by our will   From blankness and cold we fashioned stars
to our size   and signalled Aldebaran
This must we say   whoever may be to hear us
if murk devour   and none weave again in gossamer:

          These rays were ours
we made and unmade them   Not the shudder of continents
doused us   the moon's passion   nor crash of comets
In the fathomless heat of our dwarfdom   our dream's combustion
we contrived the power   the blast that snuffed us
No one bound Prometheus   Himself he chained
and consumed his own bright liver   O stranger
Plutonian   descendant   or beast in the stretching night—
there was light

As the Crow Flies
Stuart Mackinnon

An old black claw flapping
away at mere air,
flapping for weightlessness.
Unlike other birds who soar or flutter
his flying shows the effort air
sets upon bodies, for by any
quantitative measure it is
the most abrasive thing we know.
Like water it will move or be moved
only by flailing or pushing.

As the crow flies is said to be
the shortest distance between two points.
But as you look at him, you realize
the point is in the going:
he is a black point moving
over a landscape of decisions.

If crow was ambitious
he'd shuck off the air
and any idea of point to point
and take to outer space
achieving a kind of apocalypse.

But try to think of it this way:
we aren't getting any older
in this element air
we're just wearing away.

And as the crow flies it's no shorter
to where you're going unless you get there.
Where you're going is where you're at.
Think for a moment of how to
compose your face within
the decomposing air, think of how
to be graceful against this
most awkward buffeting.

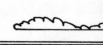

Waiting
Joy Kogawa

A very quiet
        very quiet ticking
In the room where the child
Stays by the window
Watching
While outside innumerable snow feathers
Touch melt
      touch melt
           touch melt

On Seeing
Dorothy Livesay

Far-fetched the eye of childhood sees the whole,
Essentializes figures to the brief
Recording of a rounded head
And outlets for the senses—
Eyes, ears, astonished hands;
And then takes on at puberty
A pained perception of the detailed self:
An agonizing analyst with eyes
Shaped to the comic strips
And women puffed like robins for a worm.

The inward eye begins as infantile,
Sees only the broad outline of the self;
Until some blinding day
Stricken on Damascus way
The details are revealed:
Gnarled hands of age, distorted love,
The skin of sickness stretched upon a soul;
The look "I hate," the voice "I scorn,"
The cry upon the deadly thorn.

This clarity is mercy for our sight:
Deformed, we seek the therapy of light.

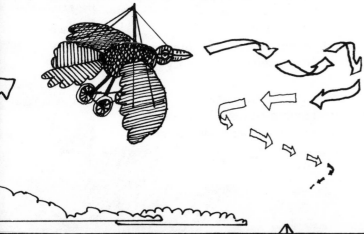

And if it is true that we acquired our knowledge before our birth, and lost it at the moment of birth, but afterward, by the exercise of our senses upon sensible objects, recover the knowledge which we had once before, I suppose that what we call learning will be the recovery of our own knowledge.

Plato, *Phaedo*

You have the same faculty as I . . . only you do not trust or cultivate it. You can see what I see, if you choose . . .

William Blake

Claude Lévi-Strauss, the French structuralist, gathered thousands of myths from different cultures and demonstrated that beyond their great diversity were even greater similarities. At the deepest level, believes Lévi-Strauss, there is an implacable pattern ingrained in the human intellect and this pattern has not changed since primitive times.

To humanists and others who believe that both man and society are perfectible, Lévi-Strauss extends small comfort. "Humanism has failed," he believes. "It has lent itself to excusing and justifying all kinds of horrors. It has misunderstood man. It has tried to cut him off from all other manifestations of nature." He is gloomy about the population explosion, the pollution of air and water and "the destruction of living species, one after another." Like many another student of past societies, he admires those primitive cultures that struck a balance between man and his natural environment.

Time, April 2, 1973

Tiger and Fox are preaching that man's survival as a species depends on finding out what kind of creature he is. "What is proposed here is not a kind of determinism," they insist. "To those who think that the law of gravity interferes with their freedom, there is nothing to say. To most sensible people, this law is simply something that has to be taken into account in dealing with the world . . . In the behavioral sphere, we may be ignoring laws just as fundamental." Man must learn from his animal heritage, or evolution will be as ruthless with him as it was with the dinosaurs, say the anthropologists who are laying their bets on the biological roots of man's behavior.

Time, April 2, 1973

Song in a Rainy Season
Stuart Mackinnon

See the rain come down
like a ton on the facetious
back of upland.

Likely in a lifetime
a ton of water falls
on each man's back,
carried unnoticed over
backbone and asscrack.

The roof heaves
its accumulation
into the drain,
that hardened artery
of certainty.

Lying on my bed
the eaves for ears
let the weight fall
on my hands.

Only hands can measure
the shift and sway
and the cruel accumulation.

Let the rain fall
on my hands as I lie
back to back
with the sudden earth.

Another aspect of human situation, closely connected
with the need for relatedness, is man's situation as a
creature, and his need to transcend this very state of the
passive creature. Man is thrown into this world without
his knowledge, consent or will, and he is removed from
it again without his consent or will. In this respect he is
not different from the animal, from the plants, or from
inorganic matter. But being endowed with reason and
imagination, he cannot be content with the passive role
of the creature, with the role of dice cast out of a cup.
He is driven by the urge to transcend the role of the
creature, the accidentalness and passivity of his
existence, by becoming a "creator".

Erich Fromm, *The Sane Society*

The Shell
James Stephens

I

And then I pressed the shell
Close to my ear,
And listened well.

And straightway, like a bell,
Came low and clear
The slow, sad, murmur of far distant seas

Whipped by an icy breeze
Upon a shore
Wind-swept and desolate.

It was a sunless strand that never bore
The footprint of a man,
Nor felt the weight

Since time began
Of any human quality or stir,
Save what the dreary winds and wave incur.

II

And in the hush of waters was the sound
Of pebbles, rolling round;
For ever rolling, with a hollow sound:

And bubbling sea-weeds, as the waters go
Swish to and fro
Their long cold tentacles of slimy grey:

There was no day;
Nor ever came a night
Setting the stars alight

To wonder at the moon:
Was twilight only, and the frightened croon,
Smitten to whimpers, of the dreary wind

And waves that journeyed blind . . .
And then I loosed an ear—Oh, it was sweet
To hear a cart go jolting down the street.

As children grow older their exploratory tendencies sometimes reach alarming proportions and adults can be heard referring to "a group of youngsters behaving like wild animals". But the reverse is actually the case. If the adults took the trouble to study the way in which adult wild animals really do behave, they would find that they are the wild animals. They are the ones who are trying to limit exploration and who are selling out to the cosiness of sub-human conservatism. Luckily for the species, there are always enough adults who retain their juvenile inventiveness and curiosity and who enable populations to progress and expand.

Desmond Morris, *The Naked Ape*

The primal powers never come to a standstill; the cycle of becoming continues uninterruptedly . . . Between the two primal powers there arises again and again a state of tension, a potential that keeps the powers in motion and causes them to unite, whereby they are constantly regenerated.

I Ching

. . . When my concepts, of myself, of you, of cars, of cows, trees and refrigerators, are shattered; and when I again face the world with a questioning attitude; when I face the being in question and *let it disclose itself to me* (it always has, but I paid it no attention after I conceptualized it); and when I re-form my concept on the basis of this newly received disclosure—then, I will suspend my concepts when my projects in life are thwarted, when my predictions about how things will act or react prove wrong. Then, if I adopt the attitude of "Let the world disclose itself to me," I will receive this disclosure and change my concepts, and I will have grown.

John Taylor, *The Shape of Minds To Come*

Noise

Jack Vance

I

Captain Hess placed a notebook on the desk and hauled a chair up under his sturdy buttocks. Pointing to the notebook, he said, "That's the property of your man Evans. He left it aboard the ship."

Galispell asked in faint surprise, "There was nothing else? No letter?"

"No, sir, not a thing. That notebook was all he had when we picked him up."

Galispell rubbed his fingers along the scarred fibers of the cover. "Understandable, I suppose." He flipped back the cover. "Hmmmm."

Hess asked tentatively, "What's been your opinion of Evans? Rather a strange chap?"

"Howard Evans? No, not at all. He's been a very valuable man to us. Why do you ask?"

Hess frowned, searching for the precise picture of Evans's behavior. "I considered him erratic, or maybe emotional."

Galispell was genuinely startled. "Howard Evans?"

Hess's eyes went to the notebook. "I took the liberty of looking through his log, and . . . well——"

"And you took the impression he was . . . strange."

"Maybe everything he writes is true," said Hess stubbornly. "But I've been poking into odd corners of space all my life and I've never seen anything like it."

"Peculiar situation," said Galispell in a neutral voice. He looked into the notebook.

II

Journal of Howard Charles Evans

I commence this journal without pessimism but certainly without optimism. I feel as if I have already died once. My time in the lifeboat was at least a foretaste of death. I flew on and on through the dark, and a coffin could be only slightly more cramped. The stars were above, below, ahead, astern. I have no clock, and I can put no duration to my drifting. It was more than a week, it was less than a year.

So much for space, the lifeboat, the stars. There are not too many pages in this journal. I will need them all to chronicle my life on this world which, rising up under me, gave me life.

There is much to tell and many ways in the telling. There is myself, my own response to this rather dramatic situation. But lacking the knack for tracing the contortions of my psyche, I will try to detail events as objectively as possible.

I landed the lifeboat on as favorable a spot as I had opportunity to select. I tested the atmosphere, temperature, pressure, and biology; then I ventured outside. I rigged an antenna and dispatched my first SOS.

Shelter is no problem; the lifeboat serves me as a bed, and, if necessary, a refuge. From sheer boredom later on I may fell a few of these trees and build a house. But I will wait; there is no urgency.

A stream of pure water trickles past the lifeboat; I have abundant concentrated food. As soon as the hydroponic tanks begin to produce, there will be fresh fruits and vegetables and yeast proteins.

Survival seems no particular problem.

The sun is a ball of dark crimson, and casts hardly more light than the full moon of Earth. The lifeboat rests on a meadow of thick black-green creeper, very pleasant underfoot. A hundred yards distant in the direction I shall call south lies a lake of inky water, and the meadow slopes smoothly down to the water's edge. Tall sprays of rather pallid vegetation—I had best use the word "trees"—bound the meadow on either side.

Behind is a hillside, which possibly continues into a range of mountains; I can't be sure. This dim red light makes vision uncertain after the first few hundred feet.

The total effect is one of haunted desolation and peace. I would enjoy the beauty of the situation if it were not for the uncertainties of the future.

The breeze drifts across the lake, smelling pleasantly fragrant, and it carries a whisper of sound from off the waves. I have assembled the hydroponic tanks and set out cultures of yeast. I shall never starve or die of thirst. The lake is smooth and inviting; perhaps in time I will build a little boat. The water is warm, but I dare not swim. What could be more terrible than to be seized from below and dragged under?

There is probably no basis for my misgivings. I have seen no animal life of any kind: no birds, fish, insects, crustacea. The world is one of absolute quiet, except for the whispering breeze.

The scarlet sun hangs in the sky, remaining in place during many of my sleeps. I see it is slowly westering; after this long day how long and how monotonous will be the night!

I have sent off four SOS sequences; somewhere a monitor station must catch them.

A machete is my only weapon, and I have been reluctant to venture far from the lifeboat. Today (if I may use the word) I took my courage in my hands and started around the lake. The trees are rather like birches, tall and supple. I think the bark and leaves would shine a clear silver in light other than this wine-colored gloom. Along the lakeshore they stand in a line, almost as if long ago they had been planted by a wandering gardener. The tall branches sway in the breeze, glinting scarlet with purple overtones, a strange and wonderful picture which I am alone to see.

I have heard it said that enjoyment of beauty is magnified in the presence of others: that a mysterious rapport comes into play to reveal subtleties which a single mind is unable to grasp. Certainly as I walked along the avenue of trees with the lake and the scarlet sun behind, I would have been grateful for companionship—but I believe that something of peace, the sense of walking in an ancient, abandoned garden, would be lost.

The lake is shaped like an hourglass; at the narrow waist I could look across and see the squat shape of the lifeboat. I sat down under a bush, which continually nodded red and black flowers in front of me.

Mist fibrils drifted across the lake and the wind made low musical sounds.

I rose to my feet, continued around the lake.

I passed through forests and glades and came once more to my lifeboat.

I went to tend my hydroponic tanks, and I think the yeast had been disturbed, prodded at curiously.

The dark red sun is sinking. Every day—it must be clear that I use "day" as the interval between my sleeps—finds it lower in the sky. Night is almost upon me, long night. How shall I spend my time in the dark?

I have no gauge other than my mind, but the breeze seems colder. It brings long, mournful chords to my ears, very sad, very sweet. Mist-wraiths go fleeting across the meadow.

Wan stars already show themselves, ghost-lamps without significance.

I have been considering the slope behind my meadow; tomorrow I think I will make the ascent.

I have plotted the position of every article I possess. I will be gone some hours; if a visitor meddles with my goods—I will know his presence for certain.

The sun is low, the air pinches at my cheeks. I must hurry if I wish to return while light still shows me the landscape. I picture myself lost; I see myself wandering the face of this world, groping for my precious lifeboat, my tanks, my meadow.

Anxiety, curiosity, obstinacy all spurring me, I set off up the slope at a half-trot.

Becoming winded almost at once, I slowed my pace. The turf of the lakeshore had disappeared; I was walking on bare rock and lichen. Below me the meadow became a patch, my lifeboat a gleaming spindle. I watched for a moment. Nothing stirred anywhere in my range of vision.

I continued up the slope and finally breasted the ridge. A vast valley fell off below me. Far away a range of great mountains stood into the dark sky. The wine-colored light slanting in from the west lit the prominences, the frontal bluffs, left the valleys in gloom: an alternate sequence of red and black beginning far in the west, continuing past, far to the east.

I looked down behind me, down to my own meadow, and was hard put to find it in the fading light. There it was, and there the lake, a sprawling hourglass. Beyond was dark forest, then a strip of old rose savanna, then a dark strip of woodland, then laminae of colorings to the horizon.

The sun touched the edge of the mountains, and with what seemed almost a sudden lurch, fell half below the horizon. I turned downslope; a terrible thing to be lost in the dark. My eye fell upon a white object, a hundred yards along the ridge. I walked nearer. Gradually it assumed form: a thimble, a cone, a pyramid—a cairn of white rocks.

A cairn, certainly. I stood looking down on it.

I turned, looked over my shoulder. Nothing in view. I looked down to the meadow. Swift shapes? I strained through the gathering murk. Nothing.

I tore at the cairn, threw rocks aside. What was below?

Nothing.

In the ground a faintly marked rectangle three feet long was perceptible. I stood back. No power I knew of could induce me to dig into that soil.

The sun was disappearing. Already at the south and north the afterglow began, lees of wine: the sun moved with astounding rapidity; what manner of sun was this, dawdling at the meridian, plunging below the horizon?

I turned downslope, but darkness came faster. The scarlet sun was gone; in the west was the sad sketch of departed flame. I stumbled, I fell. I looked into the east. A marvelous zodiacal light was forming, a strengthening blue triangle.

I watched, from my hands and knees. A cusp of bright blue lifted into the sky. A moment later a flood of sapphire washed the landscape. A new sun of intense indigo rose into the sky.

The world was the same and yet different; where my eyes had been accustomed to red and the red subcolors, now I saw the intricate cycle of blue.

When I returned to my meadow the breeze carried a new sound: bright chords that my mind could almost form into melody. For a moment I so amused myself, and thought to see dance-motion in the wisps of vapor which for the last few days had been noticeable over my meadow.

In what I will call a peculiar frame of mind I crawled into the lifeboat and went to sleep.

I crawled out of the lifeboat into an electric world. I listened. Surely that was music—faint whispers drifting in on the wind like a fragrance.

I went down to the lake, as blue as a ball of that cobalt dye so aptly known as bluing.

The music came louder; I could catch snatches of melody—sprightly, quick-step phrases. I put my hands to my ears; if I were experiencing hallucinations, the music would continue. The sound diminished, but did not fade entirely; my test was not definitive. But I felt sure it was real. And where music was there must be musicians. . . . I ran forward, shouted, "Hello!"

"Hello!" came the echo from across the lake.

The music faded a moment, as a cricket chorus quiets when disturbed, then gradually I could hear it again—distant music, "horns of elf-land faintly blowing."

It went completely out of perception. I was left standing in the blue light, alone on my meadow.

I washed my face, returned to the lifeboat, sent out another set of SOS signals.

Possibly the blue day is shorter than the red day; with no clock I can't be sure. But with my new fascination in the music and its source, the blue day seems to pass swifter.

Never have I caught sight of the musicians. Is the sound generated by the trees, by diaphanous insects crouching out of my vision?

One day I glanced across the lake, and—wonder of wonders!—a gay town spread along the opposite shore. After a first dumbfounded gaze, I ran down to the water's edge, stared as if it were the most precious sight of my life.

Pale silk swayed and rippled: pavilions, tents, fantastic edifices. . . . Who inhabited these places? I waded knee-deep into the lake, and thought to see flitting shapes.

I ran like a madman around the shore. Plants with pale blue blossoms succumbed to my feet; I left the trail of an elephant through a patch of delicate reeds.

And when I came panting to the shore opposite my meadow, what was there? Nothing.

The city had vanished like a dream. I sat down on a rock. Music came clear for an instant, as if a door had momentarily opened.

I jumped to my feet. Nothing to be seen. I looked back across the lake. There—on my meadow—a host of gauzy shapes moved like May flies over a still pond.

When I returned, my meadow was vacant. The shore across the lake was bare.

So goes the blue day; and now there is amazement to my life. Whence comes the music? Who and what are these flitting shapes, never quite real but never entirely out of mind? Four times an hour I press a hand to my forehead, fearing the symptoms of a mind turning in on itself. . . . If music actually exists on this world, actually vibrates the air, why should it come to my ears as Earth music? These chords I hear might be struck on familiar instruments; the harmonies are not at all alien. . . . And these pale plasmic wisps that I forever seem to catch from the corner of my eye: the style is that of gay and playful humanity. The tempo of their movement is the tempo of the music.

So goes the blue day. Blue air, blue-black turf, ultra-marine water, and the bright blue star bent to the west. . . . How long have I lived on this planet? I have broadcast the SOS sequence until now the batteries hiss with exhaustion; soon there will be an end to power. Food, water are no problem to me, but what use is a lifetime of exile on a world of blue and red?

The blue day is at its close. I would like to mount the slope and watch the blue sun's passing—but the remembrance of the red sunset still provokes a queasiness in my stomach. So I will watch from my meadow, and then, if there is darkness, I will crawl into the lifeboat like a bear into a cave, and wait the coming of light.

The blue day goes. The sapphire sun wanders into the western forest, the sky glooms to blue-black, the stars show like unfamiliar home-places.

For some time now I have heard no music; perhaps it has been so all-present that I neglect it.

The blue star is gone, the air chills. I think that deep night is on me indeed. . . . I hear a throb of sound, I turn my head. The east glows pale pearl. A silver globe floats up into the night: a great ball six times the diameter of Earth's full moon. Is this a sun, a satellite, a burnt-out star? What a freak of cosmology I have chanced upon!

The silver sun—I must call it a sun, although it casts a cool satin light—moves in an aureole like an oyster shell. Once again the color of the planet changes. The lake glistens like quicksilver, the trees are hammered metal. . . . The silver star passes over a high wrack of clouds, and the music seems to burst forth as if somewhere someone flung wide curtains.

I wander down to the lake. Across on the opposite shore once more I see the town. It seems clearer, more substantial; I note details that shimmered away to vagueness before—a wide terrace beside the lake, spiral columns, a row of urns. The silhouette is, I think, the same as when I saw it under the blue sun: silken tents; shimmering, reflecting cusps of light; pillars of carved stone, lucent as milk-glass; fantastic fixtures of no obvious purpose. . . . Barges drift along the quicksilver lake like moths, great sails bellying, the rigging a mesh of cobweb. Nodules of light hang on the stays, along the masts. . . . On sudden thought, I turn, look up to my own meadow. I see a row of booths as at an oldtime fair, a circle of pale stone set in the turf, a host of filmy shapes.

Step by step I edge toward my lifeboat. The music waxes. I peer at one of the shapes, but the outlines waver. It moves to the emotion of the music—or does the motion of the shape generate the music?

I run forward, shouting. One of the shapes slips past me, and I look into a blur where a face might be. I come to a halt, panting hard; I stand on the marble circle. I stamp; it rings solid. I walk toward the booths, they seem to display complex things of pale cloth and dim metal—but as I look my eyes mist over as with tears. The music goes far, far away, my meadow lies bare and quiet. My feet press into silver-black turf; in the sky hangs the silver-black star.

I am sitting with my back to the lifeboat, staring across the lake, which is still as a mirror. I have arrived at a set of theories.

My primary proposition is that I am sane—a necessary article of faith; why bother even to speculate otherwise? So—events occurring outside my own mind cause everything I have seen and heard. But—note this!—these sights and sounds do not obey the laws of science; in many respects they seem particularly subjective.

It must be, I tell myself, that both objectivity and subjectivity enter into the situation. I receive impressions which my brain finds unfamiliar, and so translates to the concept most closely related. By this theory the inhabitants of this world are constantly close; I move unknowingly through their palaces and arcades; they dance incessantly around me. As my mind gains sensitivity, I verge upon rapport with their way of life and I see them. More exactly, I sense something which creates an image in the visual region of my brain. Their emotions, the pattern of their life sets up a kind of vibration which sounds in my brain as music. . . . The reality of these creatures I am sure I will never know. They are diaphane, I am flesh; they live in a world of spirit, I plod the turf with my heavy feet.

These last days I have neglected to broadcast the SOS. Small lack; the batteries are about done.

The silver sun is at the zenith, and leans westward. What comes next? Back to the red sun? Or darkness? Certainly this is no ordinary planetary system; the course of this world along its orbit must resemble one of the pre-Copernican epicycles.

I believe that my brain is gradually tuning into phase with this world, reaching a new high level of sensitivity. If my theory is correct, the elàn-vital of the native beings expresses itself in my brain as music. On Earth we would perhaps use the word "telepathy." So I am practicing, concentrating, opening my consciousness wide to these new perceptions. Ocean mariners know a trick of never looking directly at a far light lest it strike the eyes' blind spot. I am using a similar device of never staring directly at one of the gauzy beings. I allow the image to establish itself, build itself up, and by this technique they appear quite definitely human. I sometimes think I can glimpse the features. The women are like sylphs, achingly beautiful; the men—I have not seen one in detail, but their carriage, their form is familiar.

The music is always part of the background, just as rustling of leaves is part of a forest. The mood of these creatures seems to change with their sun, so I hear music to suit. The red sun gave them passionate melancholy, the blue sun merriment. Under the silver star they are delicate, imaginative, wistful.

The silver day is on the wane. Today I sat beside the lake with the trees a screen of filigree, watching the moth-barges drift back and forth. What is their function? Can life such as this be translated in terms of economics, ecology, sociology? I doubt it. The word intelligence may not even enter the picture; is not our brain a peculiarly anthropoid characteristic, and is not intelligence a function of our peculiarly anthropoid brain? . . . A portly barge sways near, with swamp-globes in the rigging, and I forget my hypotheses. I can never know the truth, and it is perfectly possible that these creatures are no more aware of me that I originally was aware of them.

Time goes by; I return to the lifeboat. A young womanshape whirls past. I pause, peer into her face; she tilts her head, her eyes burn into mine as she passes. . . . I try an SOS—listlessly, because I suspect the batteries to be dank and dead.

And indeed they are.

The silver star is like an enormous Christmas tree bauble, round and glistening. It floats low, and once more I stand irresolute, half expecting night.

The star falls; the forest receives it. The sky dulls, and night has come.

I face the east, my back pressed to the hull of my lifeboat. Nothing.

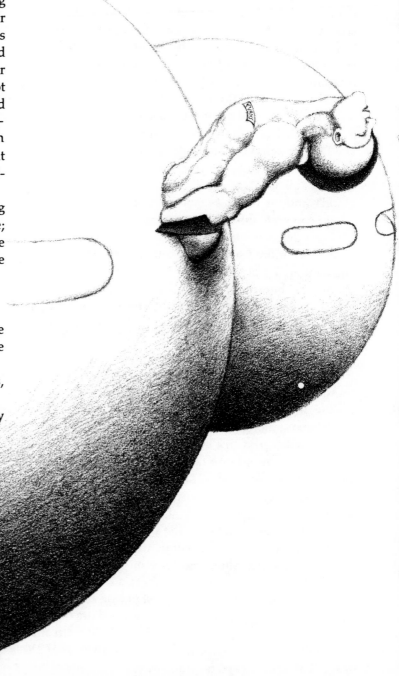

I have no conception of the passage of time. Darkness, timelessness. Somewhere clocks turn minute hands, second hands, hour hands—I stand staring into the night, perhaps as slow as a sandstone statue, perhaps as feverish as a salamander.

In the darkness there is a peculiar cessation of sound. The music has dwindled; down through a series of wistful chords, a forlorn last cry. . . .

A glow in the east, a green glow, spreading. Up rises a magnificent green sphere, the essence of all green, the tincture of emeralds, deep as the sea.

A throb of sound; rhythmical, strong music, swinging and veering.

The green light floods the planet, and I prepare for the green day.

I am almost one with the natives. I wander among their pavilions, I pause by their booths to ponder their stuffs and wares: silken medallions, spangles and circlets of woven metal, cups of fluff and iridescent puff, puddles of color and wafts of light-shot gauze. There are chains of green glass; captive butterflies; spheres which seem to hold all the heavens, all the clouds, all the stars.

And to all sides of me go the flicker and flit of the dreampeople. The men are all vague, but familiar; the women turn me smiles of ineffable provocation. But I will drive myself mad with temptations; what I see is no more than the formulation of my own brain, an interpretation. . . . And this is tragedy, for there is one creature so unutterably lovely that whenever I see the shape that is she my throat aches and I run forward, to peer into her eyes that are not eyes. . . .

Today I clasped my arms around her, expecting yielding wisp. Surprisingly, there was the feel of supple flesh. I kissed her, cheek, chin, mouth. Such a look of perplexity on the face as I have never seen; heaven knows what strange act the creature thought me to be performing.

She went her way, but the music is strong and triumphant: the voice of cornets, the resonant bass below.

A man comes past; something in his stride, his posture, plucks at my memory. I step forward; I will gaze into his face, I will plumb the vagueness.

He whirls past like a figure on a carousel; he wears

flapping ribbons of silk and pompoms of spangled satin. I pound after him, I plant myself in his path. He strides past with a side-glance, and I stare into the rigid face.

It is my own face.

He wears my face, he walks with my stride. He is I.

Already is the green day gone?

The green sun goes, and the music takes on depth. No cessation now; there is preparation, imminence. . . . What is that other sound? A far spasm of something growling and clashing like a broken gear box.

It fades out.

The green sun goes down in a sky like a peacock's tail. The music is slow, exalted.

The west fades, the east glows. The music goes toward the east, to the great bands of rose, yellow, orange, lavender. Cloud-flecks burst into flame. A golden glow consumes the sky.

The music takes on volume. Up rises the new sun—a gorgeous golden ball. The music swells into a paean of light, fulfillment, regeneration. . . . Hark! A second time the harsh sound grates across the music.

Into the sky, across the sun, drifts the shape of a spaceship. It hovers over my meadow, the landing jets come down like plumes.

The ship lands.

I hear the mutter of voices—men's voices.

The music is vanished; the marble carvings, the tinsel booths, the wonderful silken cities are gone.

III

Galispell rubbed his chin.

Captain Hess asked anxiously, "What do you think of it?"

Galispell looked for a long moment out the window. "What happened after you picked him up? Did you see any of these phenomena he talks about?"

"Not a thing." Captain Hess shook his big round head. "Sure, the system was a fantastic gaggle of dark stars and fluorescent planets and burnt-out old suns; maybe all these things played hob with his mind. He didn't seem too overjoyed to see us, that's a fact—just stood there, staring at us as if we were trespassers. 'We got your SOS,' I told him. 'Jump aboard, wrap yourself around a good meal!' He came walking forward as if his feet were dead.

"Well, to make a long story short, he finally came aboard. We loaded on his lifeboat and took off.

"During the voyage back he had nothing to do with anybody—just kept to himself, walking up and down the promenade.

"He had a habit of putting his hands to his head; one time I asked him if he was sick, if he wanted the medic to look him over. He said no, there was nothing wrong with him. That's about all I know of the man.

"We made Sun, and came down toward Earth. Personally, I didn't see what happened because I was on the bridge, but this is what they tell me:

"As Earth got bigger and bigger Evans began to act more restless than usual, wincing and turning his head back and forth. When we were about a thousand miles out, he gave a kind of furious jump.

"'The noise!' he yelled. 'The horrible *noise*!' And with that he ran astern, jumped into his lifeboat, cast off, and they tell me disappeared back the way we came.

"And that's all I got to tell you, Mr. Galispell. It's too bad, after our taking all that trouble to get him, Evans decided to pull up stakes—but that's the way it goes."

"He took off back along your course?"

"That's right. If you're wanting to ask, could he have made the planet where we found him, the answer is, not likely."

"But there's a chance?"

"Oh, sure," said Captain Hess. "There's a chance."

My Grandfather: the Thunderer
Stuart Mackinnon

My grandfather retired to a wooden
house down in the village
where the sun never set
and there were large maple trees
to the west side. He lived
there alone for twenty years
belching to the hollow house
and eating Aylmer's tomato soup.
Alone except for thunderstorms
when his hearing aid began
to crackle, and he bellowed
his responsive shouting matches
with Zeus, until a close clap
sent him fumbling for the
volume control. Lived alone
with hollow ears in a booming shade.

When the walls come tumbling down, you are left without supports, but you can also see a lot further.

R.E. Masters and J. Houston,
The Varieties of Postpsychedelic Experience

from A Separate Reality
Carlos Castaneda

"What's it like to *see*, don Juan?"

"You have to learn to *see* in order to know that. I can't tell you."

"Is it a secret I shouldn't know?"

"No. It's just that I can't describe it."

"Why?"

"It wouldn't make sense to you."

"Try me, don Juan. Maybe it'll make sense to me."

"No. You must do it yourself. Once you learn, you can *see* every single thing in the world in a different way."

"Then, don Juan, you don't see the world in the usual way anymore."

"I see both ways. When I want to *look* at the world I see it the way you do. Then when I want to *see* it I look at it the way I know and I perceive it in a different way."

"Do things look consistently the same every time you *see* them?"

"Things don't change. You change your way of looking, that's all."

"I mean, don Juan, that if you *see*, for instance, the same tree, does it remain the same every time you *see* it?"

"No. It changes and yet it's the same."

"But if the same tree changes every time you *see* it, your *seeing* may be a mere illusion."

He laughed and did not answer for some time, but seemed to be thinking. Finally he said, "Whenever you look at things you don't *see* them. You just look at them, I suppose to make sure that something is there. Since you're not concerned with *seeing*, things look very much the same every time you look at them. When you learn to *see*, on the other hand, a thing is never the same every time you *see* it, and yet it is the same. I told you, for instance, that a man is like an egg. Every time I *see* the same man I *see* an egg, yet it is not the same egg."

Danger
Louis Dudek

The poet, living in a cloud of violent dream,
congested with energy,
illuminates only as lightning does, fitfully,
with less light than thunder;
he flings plums at your feet as if they were boulders.
You will not learn from him of your danger,
you must fear a more mean and mechanical murder—
Greed, with arithmetic in his fangs, coils near you,
his tail in time and the grave;
you can hardly hear his sliding as he crawls
among the shining faces of the dead and living who sleep.

This Is a Photograph of Me
Margaret Atwood

It was taken some time ago.
At first it seems to be
a smeared
print: blurred lines and grey flecks
blended with the paper;

then, as you scan
it, you see in the left-hand corner
a thing that is like a branch: part of a tree
(balsam or spruce) emerging
and, to the right, halfway up
what ought to be a gentle
slope, a small frame house.

In the background there is a lake,
and beyond that, some low hills.

(The photograph was taken
the day after I drowned.

I am in the lake, in the center
of the picture, just under the surface.

It is difficult to say where
precisely, or to say
how large or small I am:
the effect of water
on light is a distortion

but if you look long enough,
eventually
you will be able to see me.)

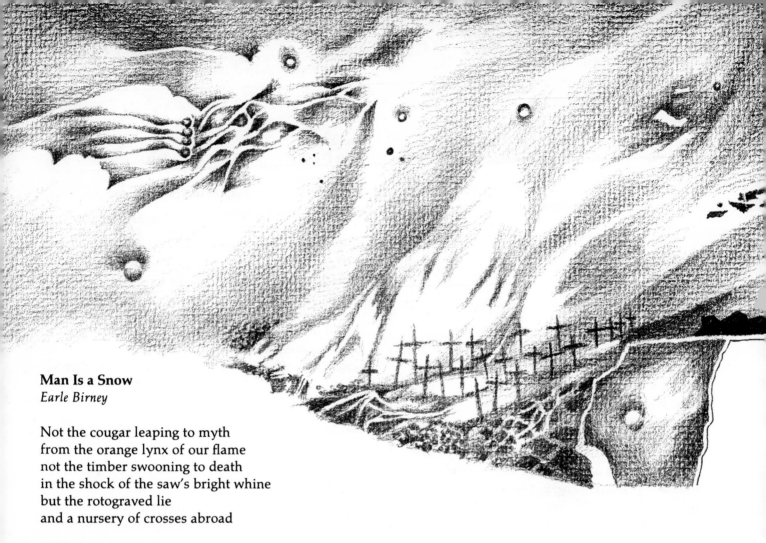

Man Is a Snow
Earle Birney

Not the cougar leaping to myth
from the orange lynx of our flame
not the timber swooning to death
in the shock of the saw's bright whine
but the rotograved lie
and a nursery of crosses abroad

Not the death of the prairie grass
in the blind wheat's unheeding
but the harvest mildewed in doubt
and the starved in the hour of our hoarding
not the rivers we foul but our blood
o cold and more devious rushing

Man is a snow that cracks
the trees' red resinous arches
and winters the cabined heart
till the chilled nail shrinks in the wall
and pistols the brittle air
till frost like ferns of the world that is lost
unfurls on the darkening window

The field of our sense-perceptions and sensations, of which we are not conscious, though we undoubtedly can infer that we possess them, that is, the dark ideas in man, is immeasurable. The clear ones, in contrast, cover infinitely few points which lie open to consciousness; so that in fact on the great map of our spirit only a few points are illuminated.

Immanuel Kant

Strength comes largely from the way in which the imagination throws a new and magic light in the common face of nature and lures us to look for some explanation. In nature is found the initial inspiration. In nature is found those exalting moments when one passed from sight to vision and pierced, to the secrets of the Universe.

Harold Bloom, *The Visionary Company*

Winter Evening
Archibald Lampman

Tonight the very horses springing by
Toss gold from whitened nostrils. In a dream
The streets that narrow to the westward gleam
Like rows of golden palaces; and high
From all the crowded chimneys tower and die
A thousand aureoles. Down in the west
The brimming plains beneath the sunset rest,
One burning sea of gold. Soon, soon shall fly
The glorious vision, and the hours shall feel
A mightier master; soon from height to height,
With silence and the sharp unpitying stars,
Stern creeping frosts, and winds that touch like steel,
Out of the depth beyond the eastern bars,
Glittering and still shall come the awful night.

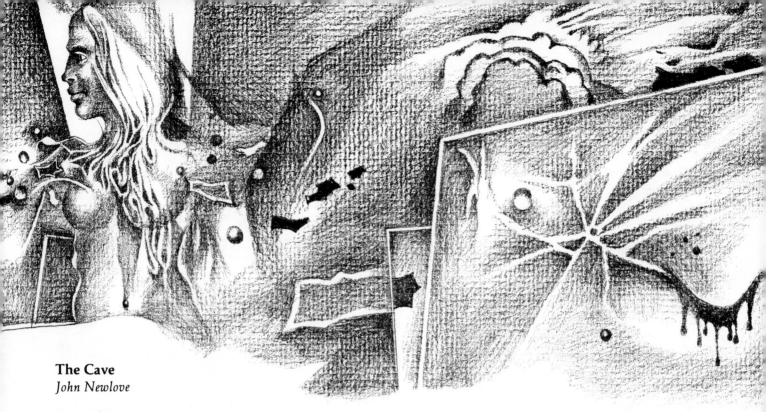

The Cave
John Newlove

The stars are your death-bed.
You rest from the cave
to Pluto or whatever dark planets
lie beyond. No ideas trap you.

In the unobstructed sunlight miles high
the Earth is beautiful as a postcard.
Sinai looks as the map says it should,
and people are too small to be observed.

In Africa there are no trees to see.
It is a map world.
The sunlight is brilliant
as a two-carat diamond on a girl's hand.

The girl is young, visible to your mind,
growing older. Beyond Pluto
and the darkest planets, children surround her.

The diamond glows on her finger
like a worm. The stars, the stars
shine like one-carat diamonds. Beyond
Pluto and the darkest planets the stars shine.

The diamonds shine in wormy rings
on fingers, in coffins of unobstructed space.
The flesh circles the bone in strips
in the coffin as the ring circled flesh.

The two-carat sun hangs loosely,
just restraining the Earth. Beyond the planets,
beyond the dark coffin, beyond the ring of stars,
your bed is in the shining, tree-lit cave.

Periodically, in mental hospital wards, aggressive patients show intense surges of activity: individuals become hostile, excitable, even violent. Such outbursts occur only sporadically but are striking enough to have invited study. At Douglas Hospital in Montreal, continuous, round-the-clock observation of patients over periods of several months did, indeed, show a picture of such periodic outbursts. Correlations between increased aggression and staff on duty, changes in menu, medication, or visiting days were too weak to explain the group behavior. Barometric pressure, temperature, humidity, and other experimental factors were juxtaposed against the hospital calendar of aggressive behavior. When no explanation could be found, Dr. Heinz Lehman compared his hospital data against data from the U.S. Space Disturbance Forecast Center in Boulder, Colorado. There appeared to be a correlation between solar flare activity (sun spots), geomagnetic disturbances, and excitement on the ward. It seemed unlikely but the study continues. Since sun flares are bursts of gaseous material, high energy particles that influence the ionosphere, causing changes in magnetic fields on earth, a relationship is not impossible. Sun storms sometimes cause a noticeable deflection in a compass needle. Perhaps, since the brain is at least as sensitive as a fine compass, it also responds to large magnetic disturbances.

We know that rats are sensitive to X-rays. . . . The human brain may also respond to such inputs. The possibility of an expanded "sensory" range has been raised by studies of biological rhythms.

Gay Gaer Luce, *Biological Rhythms in Human and Animal Physiology*

The poet is a seer, gifted with a peculiar insight into the nature of reality. And this reality is a timeless, unchanging, complete order, of which the familiar world is but a broken reflection.

Northrop Frye, *Fearful Symmetry*

Whispers of Immortality
T.S. Eliot

Webster was much possessed by death
And saw the skull beneath the skin;
And breastless creatures under ground
Leaned backward with a lipless grin.

Daffodil bulbs instead of balls
Stared from the sockets of the eyes!
He knew that thought clings round dead limbs
Tightening its lusts and luxuries.

Donne, I suppose, was such another
Who found no substitute for sense,
To seize and clutch and penetrate;
Expert beyond experience,

He knew the anguish of the marrow
The ague of the skeleton;
No contact possible to flesh
Allayed the fever of the bone.

. . . . .

Grishkin is nice: her Russian eye
Is underlined for emphasis;
Uncorseted, her friendly bust
Gives promise of pneumatic bliss.

The couched Brazilian jaguar
Compels the scampering marmoset
With subtle effluence of cat;
Grishkin has a maisonette;

The sleek Brazilian jaguar
Does not in its arboreal gloom
Distil so rank a feline smell
As Grishkin in a drawing room.

And even the Abstract Entities
Circumambulate her charm;
But our lot crawls between dry ribs
To keep our metaphysics warm.

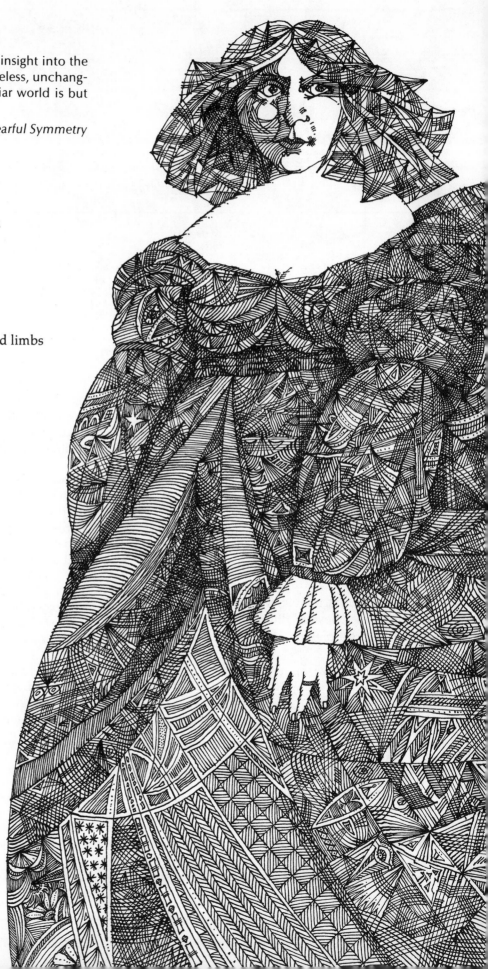

Vision is the perception of the human in all things. All nature is a projection of ourselves. As a man is, so he sees. Each person sees the universe in his own way.

William Blake

Every living thing is a symbol of everlasting powers, and it is these which one wishes to grasp and to understand.

C.M. Bowra, *The Romantic Imagination*

Compared with what we ought to be, we are only half awake. Our fires are damped, our drafts are checked. We are making use of only a small part of our possible mental and physical resources.

William James, *The Energies of Men*

Tattoo
Wallace Stevens

The light is like a spider.
It crawls over the water.
It crawls over the edges of the snow.
It crawls under your eyelids
And spreads its webs there—
Its two webs.

The webs of your eyes
Are fastened
To the flesh and bones of you
As to rafters or grass.

There are filaments of your eyes
On the surface of the water
And in the edges of the snow.

Lines Composed a Few Miles above Tintern Abbey
William Wordsworth

Five years have passed; five summers, with the length
Of five long winters! and again I hear
These waters, rolling from their mountain-springs
With a soft inland murmur. Once again
Do I behold these steep and lofty cliffs,
That on a wild secluded scene impress
Thoughts of more deep seclusion; and connect
The landscape with the quiet of the sky.
The day is come when I again repose
Here, under this dark sycamore, and view
These plots of cottage-ground, these orchard tufts,
Which at this season, with their unripe fruits,
Are clad in one green hue, and lose themselves
'Mid groves and copses. Once again I see
These hedge-rows, hardly hedge-rows, little lines
Of sportive wood run wild: these pastoral farms,
Green to the very door; and wreaths of smoke
Sent up, in silence, from among the trees!
With some uncertain notice, as might seem
Of vagrant dwellers in the houseless woods,
Or of some hermit's cave, where by his fire
The hermit sits alone.
                          These beauteous forms,
Through a long absence, have not been to me
As is a landscape to a blind man's eye;
But oft, in lonely rooms, and 'mid the din
Of towns and cities, I have owed to them,
In hours of weariness, sensations sweet,
Felt in the blood, and felt along the heart;
And passing even into my purer mind,
With tranquil restoration—feelings too
Of unremembered pleasure: such, perhaps,
As have no slight or trivial influence
On that best portion of a good man's life,
His little, nameless, unremembered acts
Of kindness and of love. Nor less, I trust,
To them I may have owed another gift,
Of aspect more sublime; that blessèd mood,
In which the burthen of the mystery,
In which the heavy and the weary weight
Of all this unintelligible world,
Is lightened—that serene and blessèd mood,
In which the affections gently lead us on—
Until, the breath of this corporeal frame
And even the motion of our human blood
Almost suspended, we are laid asleep
In body, and become a living soul;

While with an eye made quiet by the power
Of harmony, and the deep power of joy,
We see into the life of things.
                          If this
Be but a vain belief, yet, oh! how oft—
In darkness and amid the many shapes
Of joyless daylight; when the fretful stir
Unprofitable, and the fever of the world,
Have hung upon the beatings of my heart—
How oft, in spirit, have I turned to thee,
O sylvan Wye! thou wanderer through the woods,
How often has my spirit turned to thee!

    And now, with gleams of half-extinguished thought,
With many recognitions dim and faint,
And somewhat of a sad perplexity,
The picture of the mind revives again;
While here I stand, not only with the sense
Of present pleasure, but with pleasing thoughts
That in this moment there is life and food
For future years. And so I dare to hope,
Though changed, no doubt, from what I was when first
I came among these hills; when like a roe
I bounded o'er the mountains, by the sides
Of the deep rivers, and the lonely streams,
Wherever nature led: more like a man
Flying from something that he dreads than one
Who sought the thing he loved. For nature then
(The coarser pleasures of my boyish days,
And their glad animal movements all gone by)
To me was all in all—I cannot paint
What then I was. The sounding cataract
Haunted me like a passion; the tall rock,
The mountain, and the deep and gloomy wood,
Their colors and their forms, were then to me
An appetite; a feeling and a love,
That had no need of a remoter charm,
By thought supplied, nor any interest
Unborrowed from the eye. That time is past,
And all its aching joys are now no more,
And all its dizzy raptures. Not for this
Faint I, nor mourn nor murmur; other gifts
Have followed; for such loss, I would believe,
Abundant recompense. For I have learned
To look on nature, not as in the hour
Of thoughtless youth; but hearing oftentimes
The still, sad music of humanity,
Nor harsh nor grating, though of ample power
To chasten and subdue. And I have felt
A presence that disturbs me with the joy

Of elevated thoughts; a sense sublime
Of something far more deeply interfused,
Whose dwelling is the light of setting suns,
And the round ocean and the living air,
And the blue sky, and in the mind of man:
A motion and a spirit, that impels
All thinking things, all objects of all thought,
And rolls through all things. Therefore am I still
A lover of the meadows and the woods
And mountains; and of all that we behold
From this green earth; of all the mighty world
Of eye, and ear—both what they half create,
And what perceive; well pleased to recognize
In nature and the language of the sense
The anchor of my purest thoughts, the nurse,
The guide, the guardian of my heart, and soul
Of all my moral being.

                    Nor perchance,
If I were not thus taught, should I the more
Suffer my genial spirits to decay:
For thou art with me here upon the banks
Of this fair river; though my dearest Friend,
My dear, dear Friend; and in thy voice I catch
The language of my former heart, and read
My former pleasures in the shooting lights
Of thy wild eyes. Oh! yet a little while
May I behold in thee what I was once,
My dear, dear Sister! and this prayer I make,
Knowing that Nature never did betray
The heart that loved her; 'tis her privilege,
Through all the years of this our life, to lead
From joy to joy: for she can so inform
The mind that is within us, so impress
With quietness and beauty, and so feed
With lofty thoughts, that neither evil tongues,
Rash judgments, nor the sneers of selfish men,
Nor greetings where no kindness is, nor all
The dreary intercourse of daily life,
Shall e'er prevail against us, or disturb
Our cheerful faith that all which we behold
Is full of blessings. Therefore let the moon
Shine on thee in thy solitary walk;
And let the misty mountain-winds be free
To blow against thee: and, in after years,
When these wild ecstasies shall be matured
Into a sober pleasure; when thy mind
Shall be a mansion for all lovely forms,
Thy memory be as a dwelling-place
For all sweet sounds and harmonies; oh! then,

If solitude, or fear, or pain, or grief,
Should be thy portion, with what healing thoughts
Of tender joy wilt thou remember me,
And these my exhortations! Nor, perchance—
If I should be where I no more can hear
Thy voice, nor catch from thy wild eyes these gleams
Of past existence—wilt thou then forget
That on the banks of this delightful stream
We stood together; and that I, so long
A worshiper of Nature, hither came
Unwearied in that service; rather say
With warmer love—oh! with far deeper zeal
Of holier love. Nor wilt thou then forget,
That after many wanderings, many years
Of absence, these steep woods and lofty cliffs,
And this green pastoral landscape, were to me
More dear, both for themselves and for thy sake!

Everything is meaningful for a sorcerer, he said. "The sounds have holes in them and so does everything around you. Ordinarily a man does not have the speed to catch the holes, and thus he goes through life without protection. The worms, the birds, the trees, all of them can tell us unimaginable things if only one could have the speed to grasp their message. The smoke can give us that grasping speed. But we must be in good terms with all the living things of this world. This is the reason why we must talk to plants we are about to kill and apologize for hurting them; the same thing must be done with the animals we are going to hunt. We should take only enough for our needs, otherwise the plants and the animals and the worms we have killed would turn against us and cause us disease and misfortune. A warrior is aware of this and strives to appease them, so when he peers through the holes, the trees, and birds and the worms give him truthful messages."

Carlos Castaneda, *A Separate Reality*

Nature gives me my model, life and thought; the nostrils breathe, the heart beats, the lungs inhale, the being thinks, and feels, has pains and joys, ambitions, passions and emotions. These I must express. What makes my Thinker think is that he thinks not only with his brain, with his knitted brow, his distended nostrils and compressed lips, but with every muscle of his arms, back and legs, with his clenched fist and gripping toes.

   The main thing is to feel emotion, to love, to hope, to quiver, to live.

Auguste Rodin

The Man Who Was Put in a Cage

Rollo May

One evening a king of a far land was standing at his window, vaguely listening to some music drifting down the corridor from the reception room in the other wing of the palace. The king was wearied from the diplomatic reception he had just attended, and he looked out of the window pondering about the ways of the world in general and nothing in particular. His eye fell upon a man in the square below—apparently an average man, walking to the corner to take the tram home, who had taken that same route five nights a week for many years. The king followed this man in his imagination—pictured him arriving home, perfunctorily kissing his wife, eating his late meal, inquiring whether everything was right with the children, reading the paper, going to bed, perhaps engaging in the love act with his wife or perhaps not, sleeping, and getting up and going off to work again the next day.

And a sudden curiosity seized the king which for a moment banished his fatigue, "I wonder what would happen if a man were kept in a cage, like the animals at the zoo?"

So the next day the king called in a psychologist, told him of his idea, and invited him to observe the experiment. Then the king caused a cage to be brought from the zoo, and the average man was brought and placed therein.

At first the man was simply bewildered, and he kept saying to the psychologist who stood outside the cage, "I have to catch the tram, I have to get to work, look what time it is, I'll be late for work!" But later on in the afternoon the man began soberly to realize what was up, and then he protested vehemently, "The king can't do this to me! It is unjust, and against the laws." His voice was strong, and his eyes full of anger.

During the rest of the week the man continued his vehement protests. When the king would walk by the cage, as he did every day, the man made his protests directly to the monarch. But the king would answer, "Look here, you get plenty of food, you have a good bed, and you don't have to work. We take good care of you—so why are you objecting?" Then after some days the man's protests lessened and then ceased. He was silent in his cage, refusing generally to talk, but the psychologist could see hatred glowing like a deep fire in his eyes.

But after several weeks the psychologist noticed that more and more it now seemed as if the man were pausing a moment after the king's daily reminder to him that he was being taken good care of—for a second the hatred was postponed from returning to his eyes—as though he were asking himself if what the king said were possibly true.

And after a few weeks more, the man began to discuss with the psychologist how it was a useful thing if a man were given food and shelter, and that man had to live by his fate in any case and the part of wisdom was to accept his fate. So when a group of professors and graduate students came in one day to observe the man in the cage, he was friendly toward them and explained to them that he had chosen this way of life, that there are great values in security and being taken care of, that they would of course see how sensible his course was, and so on. How strange! thought the psychologist, and how pathetic—why is it he struggles so hard to get them to approve of his way of life?

In the succeeding days when the king would walk through the courtyard, the man would fawn upon him from behind the bars in his cage and thank him for the food and shelter. But when the king was not in the yard and the man was not aware that the psychologist was present, his expression was quite different—sullen and morose. When his food was handed to him through the bars by the keeper, the man would often drop the dishes or dump over the water and then be embarrassed because of his stupidity and clumsiness. His conversation became increasingly one-tracked: and instead of the involved philosophical theories about the value of being taken care of, he had gotten down to simple sentences like "It is fate," which he would say over and over again, or just mumble to himself, "It is."

It was hard to say just when the last phase set in. But the psychologist became aware that the man's face seemed to have no particular expression: his smile was no longer fawning, but simply empty and meaningless, like the grimace a baby makes when there is gas on its stomach. The man ate his food, and exchanged a few sentences with the psychologist from time to time; his eyes were distant and vague, and though he looked at the psychologist, it seemed that he never really *saw* him.

And now the man, in his desultory conversations, never used the word "I" any more. He had accepted the cage. He had no anger, no hate, no rationalizations. But he was now insane.

That night the psychologist sat in his parlor trying to write a concluding report. But it was very difficult for him to summon up words, for he felt within himself a great emptiness. He kept trying to reassure himself with the words, "They say that nothing is ever lost, that matter is merely changed to energy and back again." But he couldn't help feeling something *had* been lost, something had been taken out of the universe in this experiment, and there was left only a void.

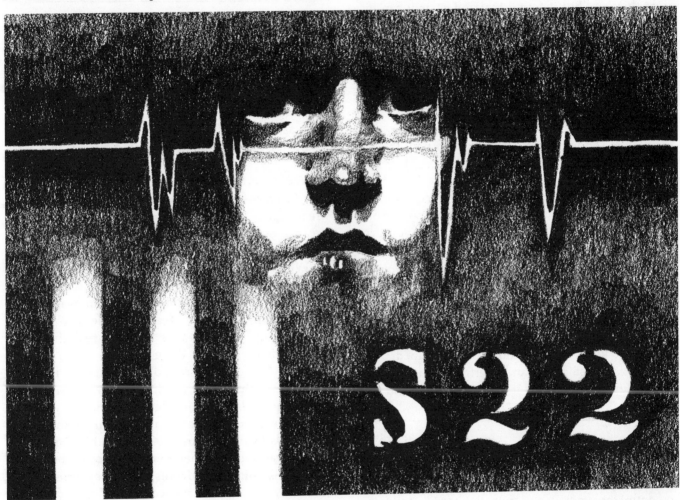

For animals lack both kinds of imagination. They plainly lack the scientific imagination to invent, say, the electric current. But they also lack the poetic imagination, the ability to enter the feelings of others from the inside, that shudders yet delights to give an electric shock—in fun or in the torture chamber. Animals do not devise the concentration camps, because they are not clever enough, of course. But neither do they staff them; it is not true that the camps were run by beasts—they were run by men; the pleasure is as peculiar to man as the invention.

J. Bronowski, *The Identity of Man*

For too many maturity means a narrowing into a dull or resigned acceptance of a limited representative self and a disavowal or oblivion of the real self. Similarly, too much teaching offers insufficient opportunity and too feeble a provocation to enrich the image of self by imaginative participation in many modes of being; just as, all too frequently, it is, in face of the helplessness of the child, an unjust invasion of the real self.

William Walsh, *The Use of Imagination*

The Tale of the Sands

Idries Shah

A stream, from its source in far-off mountains, passing through every kind and description of countryside, at last reached the sands of the desert. Just as it had crossed every other barrier, the stream tried to cross this one, but it found that as fast as it ran into the sand, its waters disappeared.

It was convinced, however, that its destiny was to cross this desert, and yet there was no way. Now a hidden voice, coming from the desert itself, whispered: 'The Wind crosses the desert, and so can the stream.'

The stream objected that it was dashing itself against the sand, and only getting absorbed: that the wind could fly, and this was why it could cross a desert.

'By hurtling in your own accustomed way you cannot get across. You will either disappear or become a marsh. You must allow the wind to carry you over, to your destination.'

But how could this happen? 'By allowing yourself to be absorbed in the wind.'

This idea was not acceptable to the stream. After all, it had never been absorbed before. It did not want to lose its individuality. And, once having lost it, how was one to know that it could ever be regained?

'The wind', said the sand, 'performs this function. It takes up water, carries it over the desert, and then

---

In archery a man must die to his purer nature, the one which is free from all artificiality and deliberation, if he is to reach perfect enjoyment of Tao. He must learn how to control the emittance of truth, flowing like an eternal spring. Finally, he must be able to reveal Tao in his own attitude on the basis of true "insight." This way is a very easy and direct one. The most difficult thing is to let oneself die completely in the very act of shooting.

Karlfried von Durkheim, *The Japanese Cult of Tranquility*

Mysticism strives to piece together the fragments broken by the religious cataclysm, to bring back the old unity which religion has destroyed, but on a new plane, where the world of mythology and that of revelation meet in the soul of man.

Gershom G. Scholem, *Major Trends in Jewish Mysticism*

---

lets it fall again. Falling as rain, the water again becomes a river.'

'How can I know that this is true?'

'It is so, and if you do not believe it, you cannot become more than a quagmire, and even that could take many, many years; and it certainly is not the same as a stream.'

'But can I not remain the same stream that I am today?'

'You cannot in either case remain so,' the whisper said. 'Your essential part is carried away and forms a stream again. You are called what you are even today because you do not know which part of you is the essential one.'

When he heard this, certain echoes began to arise in the thoughts of the stream. Dimly, he remembered a state in which he—or some part of him, was it?—had been held in the arms of a wind. He also remembered—or did he?—that this was the real thing, not necessarily the obvious thing, to do.

And the stream raised his vapour into the welcoming arms of the wind, which gently and easily bore it upwards and along, letting it fall softly as soon as they reached the roof of a mountain, many, many miles away. And because he had had his doubts, the stream was able to remember and record more strongly in his mind the details of the experience. He reflected, 'Yes, now I have learned my true identity.'

The stream was learning. But the sands whispered: 'We know, because we see it happen day after day: and because we, the sands, extend from the riverside all the way to the mountain.'

And that is why it is said that the way in which the Stream of Life is to continue on its journey is written in the Sands.

**Not Ideas About The Thing
But The Thing Itself**
Wallace Stevens

At the earliest ending of winter,
In March, a scrawny cry from outside
Seemed like a sound in his mind.

He knew that he heard it,
A bird's cry, at daylight or before,
In the early March wind.

The sun was rising at six,
No longer a battered panache above snow . . .
It would have been outside.

It was not from the vast ventriloquism
Of sleep's faded papier-mâché . . .
The sun was coming from outside.

That scrawny cry—it was
A chorister whose c preceded the choir.
It was part of the colossal sun,

Surrounded by its choral rings,
Still far away. It was like
A new knowledge of reality.

Because of modern man's overdevelopment of the linguistic (symbolic) parts of his brain, he has all but forgotten the ESP potentialities that would have made him a true "sensitive" in the way that innumerable animals are sensitive–sensitive that is, to means of communication that we cannot understand. Along with this has gone a "sense of the world", which we have lost, to our great detriment. However, since man is a phylo-genetically young animal, this tremendous, recent drive toward "language-thinking" has not entirely eliminated man's capacity for regaining the "forgotten senses" that reside in more primitive modes–those connected with the most ancient channels such as imagery and emotion–but not language.

D.E. Carr, *The Forgotten Senses*

The moon, the snow,
　And now besides—through mist,
　　the morning glow!

Michihko

A deer along with it,
　the mountain's shadow at the temple gate—
　　the setting sun.

Buson

The moon on the pine:
　I keep hanging it—taking it off—
　　and gazing each time.

Hokushi

A lightning gleam:
　into darkness travels
　　a night heron's scream.

Basho

If we insist on deriving the vision from a personal experience, we must treat the former as something secondary—as a mere substitute for reality. The result is that we strip the vision of its primordial quality and take it as nothing but a symptom. The pregnant chaos then shrinks to the proportions of a psychic disturbance. With this account of the matter we feel reassured and turn again to our picture of a well-ordered cosmos. Since we are practical and reasonable, we do not expect the cosmos to be perfect; we accept these unavoidable imperfections which we call abnormalities and diseases, and we take it for granted that human nature is not exempt from them. The frightening revelation of abysses that defy the human understanding is dismissed as illusion, and the poet is regarded as a victim and perpetrator of deception. Even to the poet, his primordial experience was "human—all too human", to such a degree that he could not face its meaning but had to conceal it from himself.

C.G. Jung, *Modern Man in Search of a Soul*

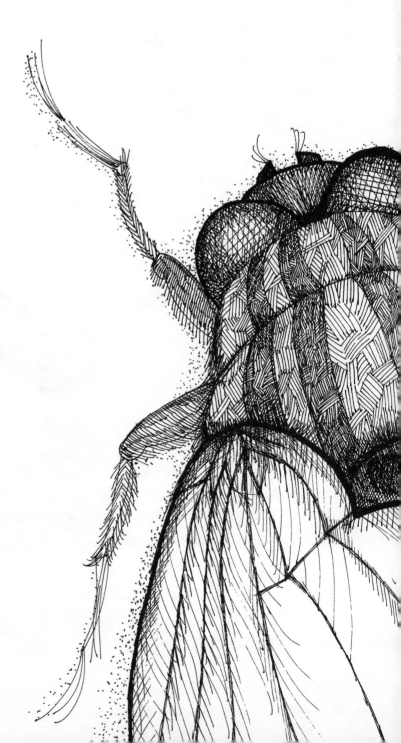

This Whole
Of suns, and worlds, and men, and beasts, and flowers,
With all the silent or tempestuous workings
By which they have been, are, or cease to be,
Is but a vision;—all that it inherits
Are motes of a sick eye, bubbles and dreams;
Thought is its cradle, and its grave, nor less
The future and the past are idle shadows
Of thought's eternal flight—they have no being:
Nought is but that which feels itself to be.

Percy Bysshe Shelley

In a dark tree there hides
A bough, all golden, leaf and pliant stem,
Sacred to Proserpine. This all the grove
Protects, and shadows cover it with darkness.
Until this bough, this bloom of light, is found,
No one receives his passport to the darkness
Whose queen requires this tribute. In succession,
After the bough is plucked, another grows,
Gold-Green with the same metal. Raise the eyes,
Look up, reach up the hand.

Sanity today appears to rest very largely on a capacity to adapt to the external world—the interpersonal world, and the realm of human collectives.

As this external human world is almost completely and totally estranged from the inner, any personal direct awareness of the inner world has already grave risks.

But since society, without knowing it, is *starving* for the inner, the demands on people to evoke its presence in a "safe" way, in a way that need not be taken seriously, etc., is tremendous.

R.D. Laing, *The Politics of Experience*

To be enlightened is to be aware, always, of total reality in its immanent otherness—to be aware of it and yet to remain in a condition to survive as an animal, to think and feel as a human being, to resort whenever expedient to systematic reasoning. Our goal is to discover that we have always been where we ought to be.

Aldous Huxley, *The Doors of Perception*

A man, just one—
  also a fly, just one—
    in the huge drawing room.

Issau

On the temple bell
  has settled, and is fast asleep,
    a butterfly.

Buson

Icy the moonshine:
  shadow of a tombstone,
    shadow of a pine.

Kyoshi

No sky at all;
  no earth at all—and still
    the snowflakes fall. . . .

Hashin

Catching the Ox

Long lost in the wilderness, the boy has at last found the ox and his hands
are on him. But, owing to the overwhelming pressure of the outside
world, the ox is hard to keep under control. The wild nature
is still unruly, and altogether refuses to be broken. If the oxherd wishes to see
the ox completely in harmony with himself, he has surely to use
the whip freely. With the energy of his whole being, the boy has at last taken hold
of the ox: But how wild his will, how ungovernable his power!

Herding the Ox

When a thought moves, another follows, and then another—an endless train
of thoughts is thus awakened. Through enlightenment all this turns
into truth; but falsehood asserts itself when confusion prevails. Things oppress us
not because of an objective world, but because of a self-deceiving mind.
The boy is not to separate himself with his whip and tether, lest the animal should
wander away into a world of defilements; when the ox is properly
tended to, he will grow pure and docile; without a chain, nothing binding,
he will by himself follow the oxherd.

Frost at Midnight
Samuel Taylor Coleridge

The frost performs its secret ministry,
Unhelped by any wind. The owlet's cry
Came loud—and hark, again! loud as before.
The inmates of my cottage, all at rest,
Have left me to that solitude, which suits
Abstruser musings: save that at my side
My cradled infant slumbers peacefully.
'Tis calm indeed! so calm, that it disturbs
And vexes meditation with its strange
And extreme silentness. Sea, hill, and wood,
This populous village! Sea, and hill, and wood,
With all the numberless goings-on of life,
Inaudible as dreams! the thin blue flame
Lies on my low-burnt fire, and quivers not;
Only that film, which fluttered on the grate,
Still flutters there, the sole unquiet thing.
Methinks, its motion in this hush of nature
Gives it dim sympathies with me who live,
Making it a companionable form,
Whose puny flaps and freaks the idling Spirit
By its own moods interprets, every where
Echo or mirror seeking of itself,
And makes a toy of Thought.

                  But O! how oft,
How oft, at school, with most believing mind,
Presageful, have I gazed upon the bars,
To watch that fluttering *stranger!* and as oft
With unclosed lids, already had I dreamt
Of my sweet birth-place, and the old church-tower,
Whose bells, the poor man's only music, rang
From morn to evening, all the hot Fair-day,
So sweetly, that they stirred and haunted me
With a wild pleasure, falling on mine ear
Most like articulate sounds of things to come!
So gazed I, till the soothing things, I dreamt,
Lulled me to sleep, and sleep prolonged my dreams!
And so I brooded all the following morn,
Awed by the stern preceptor's face, mine eye
Fixed with mock study on my swimming book:
Save if the door half opened, and I snatched
A hasty glance, and still my heart leaped up,
For still I hoped to see the *stranger's* face,
Townsman, or aunt, or sister more beloved,
My play-mate when we both were clothed alike!

   Dear Babe, that sleepest cradled by my side,
Whose gentle breathings, heard in this deep calm,
Fill up the interspersèd vacancies
And momentary pauses of the thought!
My babe so beautiful! it thrills my heart
With tender gladness, thus to look at thee,
And think that thou shalt learn far other lore,
And in far other scenes! For I was reared
In the great city, pent 'mid cloisters dim,
And saw nought lovely but the sky and stars.
But *thou*, my babe! shalt wander like a breeze
By lakes and sandy shores, beneath the crags
Of ancient mountain, and beneath the clouds,
Which image in their bulk both lakes and shores
And mountain crags: so shalt thou see and hear
The lovely shapes and sounds intelligible
Of that eternal language, which thy God
Utters, who from eternity doth teach
Himself in all, and all things in himself.
Great universal Teacher! he shall mould
Thy spirit, and by giving make it ask.

   Therefore all seasons shall be sweet to thee,
Whether the summer clothe the general earth
With greenness, or the redbreast sit and sing
Betwixt the tufts of snow on the bare branch
Of mossy apple-tree, while the night thatch
Smokes in the sun-thaw; whether the eave-drops fall
Heard only in the trances of the blast,
Or if the secret ministry of frost
Shall hang them up in silent icicles,
Quietly shining to the quiet Moon.

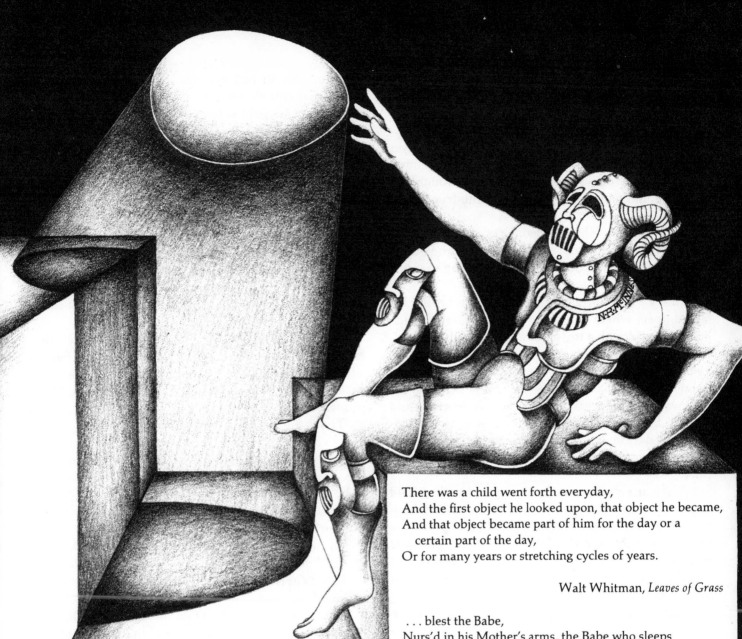

There was a child went forth everyday,
And the first object he looked upon, that object he became,
And that object became part of him for the day or a
     certain part of the day,
Or for many years or stretching cycles of years.

Walt Whitman, *Leaves of Grass*

. . . blest the Babe,
Nurs'd in his Mother's arms, the Babe who sleeps
Upon his Mother's breast, who, when his soul,
Claims manifest kindred with an earthly soul,
Doth gather passion from his Mother's eye! . . .
     Thus, day by day,
Subjected to the discipline of love,
His organs and recipient faculties
Are quicken'd, are more vigorous, his mind spreads,
Tenacious of the forms which it receives.

William Wordsworth

The joy of the child is so complete, so self-delighting, because it is the accompaniment of those primary movements of the imagination by which he discovers and furthers his humanity, and finds and increases his freedom.

William Walsh, *The Use of Imagination*

But we are separated from the child by a more impassable obstacle. The child accepts the amazing universe. He is astounded by it but never despairs of it. He supposes an answer to exist for every question, and his chief difficulty is to articulate the question. His world is undisturbed by doubt. "The deep intuition of our oneness" with childhood, which is the condition of an imaginative perception of it, is possible only in an age of firmer certainties and fewer uncertainties than our own. But we live in an alien Cartesian world, under the jurisdiction of doubt, and we neither speak nor understand the language of the child.

William Walsh, *The Use of Imagination*

Hush!

Zenna Henderson

June sighed and brushed her hair back from her eyes automatically as she marked her place in her geometry book with one finger and looked through the dining-room door at Dubby lying on the front-room couch.

"Dubby, *please*," she pleaded. "You promised your mother that you'd be quiet tonight. How can you get over your cold if you bounce around making so much noise?"

Dubby's fever-bright eyes peered from behind his tented knees where he was holding a tin truck which he hammered with a toy guitar.

"I am quiet, June. It's the truck that made the noise. See?" And he banged on it again. The guitar splintered explosively and Dubby blinked in surprise. He was wavering between tears at the destruction and pleased laughter for the awful noise it made. Before he could decide, he began to cough, a deep-chested pounding cough that shook his small body unmercifully.

"That's just about enough out of you, Dubby," said June firmly, clearing the couch of toys and twitching the covers straight with a practiced hand. "You have to go to your room in just fifteen minutes anyway—or right now if you don't settle down. Your mother will be calling at seven to see if you're okay. I don't want to have to tell her you're worse because you wouldn't be good. Now read your book and keep quiet. I've got work to do."

There was a brief silence broken by Dubby's sniffling and June's scurrying pencil. Then Dubby began to chant:

"Shrimp boatses running a dancer tonight
Shrimp boatses running a dancer tonight
Shrimp boatses *running a dancer tonight*
SHRIMP BOATSes RUNning a DANCer to-NIGHT—"

"Dub-by!" called June, frowning over her paper at him.

"That's not noise," protested Dubby. "It's singing. *Shrimp boatses*—" The cough caught him in mid-phrase and June busied herself providing Kleenexes and comfort until the spasm spent itself.

"See?" she said. "Your cough thinks it's noise."

"Well, what can I do then?" fretted Dubby, bored by four days in bed and worn out by the racking cough that still shook him. "I can't sing and I can't play. I want something to do."

"Well," June searched the fertile pigeonholes of her baby sitter's repertoire and came up with an idea that Dubby had once originated himself and dearly loved.

"Why not play-like? Play-like a zoo. I think a green giraffe with a mop for a tail and roller skates for feet would be nice, don't you?"

Dubby considered the suggestion solemnly. "If he had egg beaters for ears," he said, overly conscious as always of ears, because of the trouble he so often had with his own.

"Of course he does," said June. "Now you play-like one."

"Mine's a lion," said Dubby, after mock consideration. "Only he has a flag for a tail—a pirate flag—and he wears yellow pajamas and airplane wings sticking out of his back and his ears turn like propellers."

"That's a good one," applauded June. "Now mine is an eagle with rainbow wings and roses growing around his neck. And the only thing he ever eats is the song of birds, but the birds are scared of him and so he's hungry nearly all the time—pore ol'iggle!"

Dubby giggled. "Play-like some more," he said, settling back against the pillows.

"No, it's your turn. Why don't you play-like by yourself now? I've just got to get my geometry done."

Dubby's face shadowed and then he grinned. "Okay."

June went back to the table, thankful that Dubby was a nice kid and not like some of the brats she had met in her time. She twined both legs around the legs of her chair, running both hands up through her hair. She paused before tackling the next problem to glance in at Dubby. A worry nudged at her heart as she saw how pale and fine-drawn his features were. It seemed, everytime she came over, he was more nearly transparent.

She shivered a little as she remembered her mother saying, "Poor child. He'll never have to worry about old age. Have you noticed his eyes, June? He has wisdom in them now that no child should have. He has looked too often into the Valley."

June sighed and turned to her work.

The heating system hummed softly and the out-of-joint day settled into a comfortable accustomed evening.

Mrs. Warren rarely ever left Dubby because he was ill so much of the time, and she practically never left him until he was settled for the night. But today when June got home from school, her mother had told her to call Mrs. Warren.

"Oh, June," Mrs. Warren had appealed over the phone, "could you possibly come over right now?"

"Now?" asked June, dismayed, thinking of her hair and nails she'd planned to do, and the tentative date with Larryanne to hear her new album.

"I hate to ask it," said Mrs. Warren. "I have no patience with people who make last minute arrangements, but Mr. Warren's mother is very ill again and we just have to go over to her house. We wouldn't trust Dubby with anyone but you. He's got that nasty bronchitis again, so we can't take him with us. I'll get home as soon as I can, even if Orin has to stay. He's home from work right now, waiting for me. So please come, June!"

"Well," June melted to the tears in Mrs. Warren's voice. She could let her hair and nails and album go and she could get her geometry done at the Warrens' place. "Well, okay. I'll be right over."

"Oh, bless you, child," cried Mrs. Warren. Her voice faded away from the phone. "Orin, she's coming—" and the receiver clicked.

"June!" He must have called several times before June began to swim back up through the gloomy haze of the new theorem.

"Joo-un!" Dubby's plaintive voice reached down to her and she signed in exasperation. She had nearly figured out how to work the problem.

"Yes, Dubby." The exaggerated patience in her voice signaled her displeasure to him.

"Well," he faltered, "I don't want to play-like anymore. I've used up all my thinkings. Can I make something now? Something for true?"

"Without getting off the couch?" asked June cautiously, wise from past experience.

"Yes," grinned Dubby.

"Without my to-ing and fro-ing to bring you stuff?" she questioned, still wary.

"Uh-huh," giggled Dubby.

"What can you make for true without anything to make it with?" June asked skeptically.

Dubby laughed. "I just thought it up." Then all in one breath, unable to restrain his delight: "It's-really-kinda-like-play-like, but-I'm going-to-make-something-that-isn't-like-anything-real-so it'll-be-for-true, cause-it-won't-be-play-like-anything-that's-real!"

"Huh? Say that again," June challenged. "I bet you can't do it."

Dubby was squirming with excitement. He coughed tentatively, found it wasn't a prelude to a full production and said: "I can't say it again, but I can do it, I betcha. Last time I was sick, I made up some new magic words. They're real good. I betcha they'll work real good like anything."

"Okay, go ahead and make something," said June. "Just so it's quiet."

"Oh, it's *real* quiet," said Dubby in a hushed voice. "Exter quiet. I'm going to make a Noise-eater."

"A Noise-eater?"

"Uh-huh!" Dubby's eyes were shining. "It'll eat up all the noises. I can make lotsa racket then, 'cause it'll eat it all up and make it real quiet for you so's you can do your jommety."

"Now that's right thunkful of you, podner," drawled June. "Make it a good one, because little boys make a lot of noise."

"Okay." And Dubby finally calmed down and settled back against his pillows.

The heating system hummed. The old refrigerator in the kitchen cleared its throat and added its chirking throb to the voice of the house. The mantel clock tocked firmly to itself in the front room. June was absorbed in her homework when a flutter of movement at her elbow jerked her head up.

"Dubby!" she began indignantly.

"Shh!" Dubby pantomimed, finger to lips, his eyes wide with excitement. He leaned against June, his fever radiating like a small stove through his pajamas and robe. His breath was heavy with the odor of illness as he put his mouth close to her ear and barely whispered.

"I made it. The Noise-eater. He's asleep now. Don't make a noise or he'll get you."

"I'll get you, too," said June. "Play-like is play-like, but you get right back on that couch!"

"I'm too scared," breathed Dubby. "What if I cough?"

"You will cough if you—" June started in a normal tone, but Dubby threw himself into her lap and muffled her mouth with his small hot hand. He was trembling.

"Don't! Don't!" he begged frantically. "I'm scared. How do you un-play-like? I didn't know it'd work so good!"

There was a *choonk* and a slither in the front room. June strained her ears, alarm stirring in her chest.

"Don't be silly," she whispered. "Play-like isn't for true. There's nothing in there to hurt you."

A sudden succession of musical pings startled June and threw Dubby back into her arms until she recognized Mrs. Warren's bedroom clock striking seven o'clock—early as usual. There was a soft, drawn-out slither in the front room and then silence.

"Go on, Dubby. Get back on the couch like a nice child. We've played long enough."

"You take me."

June herded him ahead of her, her knees bumping his reluctant back at every step until he got a good look at the whole front room. Then he sighed and relaxed.

"He's gone," he said normally.

"Sure he is," replied June. "Play-like stuff always goes away." She tucked him under his covers. Then, as if hoping to brush his fears—and hers—away, by calmly discussing it, "What did he look like?"

"Well, he had a body like Mother's vacuum cleaner—the one that lies down on the floor—and his legs were like my sled, so he could slide on the floor, and had a nose like the hose on the cleaner only he was able to make it long or short when he wanted to."

Dubby, overstrained, leaned back against his pillows.

The mantel clock began to boom the hour deliberately.

"And he had little eyes like the light inside the refrigerator—"

June heard a *choonk* at the hall door and glanced up. Then with fear-stiffened lips, she continued for him, "And ears like TV antennae because he needs good ears to find the noises." And watched, stunned, as the round metallic body glided across the floor on shiny runners and paused in front of the clock that was deliberating on the sixth stroke.

The long, wrinkly trunk-like nose on the front of the thing flashed upward. The end of it shimmered, then melted into the case of the clock. And the seventh stroke never began. There was a soft sucking sound and the nose dropped free. On the mantel, the hands of the clock dropped soundlessly to the bottom of the dial.

In the tight circle of June's arms, Dubby whimpered. June clapped her hand over his mouth. But his shoulders began to shake and he rolled frantic imploring eyes at her as another coughing spell began. He couldn't control it.

June tried to muffle the sound with her shoulder, but over the deep, hawking convulsions, she heard the *choonk* and slither of the creature and screamed as she felt it nudge her knee. Then the long snout nuzzled against her shoulder and she heard a soft hiss as it touched the straining throat of the coughing child. She grabbed the horribly vibrating thing and tried to pull it away, but Dubby's cough cut off in mid-spasm.

In the sudden quiet that followed she heard a gurgle like a straw in the bottom of a soda glass and Dubby folded into himself like an empty laundry bag. June tried to straighten him against the pillows, but he slid laxly down.

June stood up slowly. Her dazed eyes wandered trance-like to the clock, then to the couch, then to the horrible thing that lay beside it. Its glowing eyes were blinking and its ears shifting planes—probably to locate sound.

Her mouth opened to let out the terror that was constricting her lungs, and her frantic scream coincided with the shrill clamor of the telephone. The Eater hesitated, then slid swiftly toward the repeated ring. In the pause after the party line's four identifying rings, it stopped and June clapped both hands over her mouth, her eyes dilated with paralyzed terror.

The ring began again. June caught Dubby up into her arms and backed slowly toward the front door. The Eater's snout darted out to the telephone and the ring stilled without even an after-resonance.

The latch of the front door gave a rasping click under June's trembling hand. Behind her, she heard the *choonk* and horrible slither as the Eater lost interest in the silenced telephone. She whirled away from the door, staggering off balance under the limp load of Dubby's body. She slipped to one knee, spilling the child to the floor with a thump. The Eater slid toward her, pausing at the hall door, its ears tilting and moving.

June crouched on her knees, staring, one hand caught under Dubby. She swallowed convulsively, then cautiously withdrew her hand. She touched Dubby's bony little chest. There was no movement. She hesitated indecisively, then backed away, eyes intent on the Eater.

Her heart drummed in her burning throat. Her blood roared in her ears. The starchy *krunkle* of her wide skirt rattled in the stillness. The fibers of the rug murmured under her knees and toes. She circled wider, wider, the noise only loud enough to hold the Eater's attention—not to attract him to her. She backed guardedly into the corner by the radio. Calculatingly, she reached over and clicked it on, turning the volume dial as far as it would go.

The Eater slid tentatively toward her at the click of the switch. June backed slowly away, eyes intent on the creature. The sudden insane blare of the radio hit her an almost physical blow. The Eater glided up close against the vibrating cabinet, its snout lifting and drinking in the horrible cacophony of sound.

June lurched for the front door, wrenching frantically at the door knob. She stumbled outside, slamming the door behind her. Trembling, she sank to the top step, wiping the cold sweat from her face with the under side of her skirt. She shivered in the sharp cold, listening to the raucous outpouring from the radio that boomed so loud it was no longer intelligible.

She dragged herself to her feet, pausing irresolutely, looking around at the huddled houses, each set on its own acre of weeds and lawn. They were all dark in the early winter evening.

June gave a little moan and sank on the step again, hugging herself desperately against the penetrating chill. It seemed an eternity that she crouched there before the radio cut off in mid-note.

Fearfully, she roused and pressed her face to one of the door panes. Dimly through the glass curtains she could see the Eater, sluggish and swollen, lying quietly by the radio. Hysteria was rising for a moment, but she resolutely knuckled the tears from her eyes.

The headlights scythed around the corner, glittering swiftly across the blank windows next door as the car crunched into the Warrens' driveway and came to a gravel-skittering stop.

June pressed her hands to her mouth, sure that even through the closed door she could hear the *choonk* and slither of the thing inside as it slid to and fro, seeking sound.

The car door slammed and hurried footsteps echoed along the path. June made wild shushing motions with her hands as Mrs. Warren scurried around the corner of the house.

"June!" Mrs. Warren's voice was ragged with worry. "Is Dubby all right? What are you doing out here? What's wrong with the phone?" She fumbled for the door knob.

"No, no!" June shouldered her roughly aside. "Don't go in! It'll get you, too!"

She heard a thud just inside the door. Dimly through the glass she saw the flicker of movement as the snout of the Eater raised and wavered toward them.

"June!" Mrs. Warren jerked her away from the door. "Let me in! What's the matter? Have you gone crazy?"

Mrs. Warren stopped suddenly, her face whiten-

ing. *"What have you done to Dubby, June?"*

The girl gulped with the shock of the accusation. "I haven't done anything, Mrs. Warren. He made a Noise-eater and it—it—" June winced away from the sudden blaze of Mrs. Warren's eyes.

"Get away from that door!" Mrs. Warren's face was that of a stranger, her words icy and clipped. "I trusted you with my child. If anything has happened to him—"

"Don't go in—oh, don't go in!" June grabbed at her coat hysterically. "Please, please wait! Let's get—"

"Let go!" Mrs. Warren's voice grated between her tightly clenched teeth. "Let me go, you—you—" Her hand flashed out and the crack of her palm against June's cheek was echoed by a *choonk* inside the house. June was staggered by the blow, but she clung to the coat until Mrs. Warren pushed her sprawling down the front steps and fumbled at the knob, crying, "Dubby! Dubby!"

June, scrambling up the steps on hands and knees, caught a glimpse of a hovering something that lifted and swayed like a waiting cobra. It was slapped aside by the violent opening of the door as Mrs. Warren stumbled into the house, her cries suddenly stilling on her slack lips as she saw her crumpled son by the couch.

She gasped and whispered, "Dubby!" She lifted him into her arms. His head rolled loosely against her shoulder. Her protesting, "No, no, no!" merged into half-articulate screams as she hugged him to her.

And from behind the front door there was a *choonk* and a slither.

June lunged forward and grabbed the reaching thing that was homing in on Mrs. Warren's hysterical grief. Her hands closed around it convulsively, her whole weight dragging backward, but it had a strength she couldn't match. Desperately then, her fists clenched, her eyes tight shut, she screamed and screamed and screamed.

The snout looped almost lazily around her straining throat, but she fought her way almost to the front door before the thing held her, feet on the floor, body at an impossible angle and stilled her frantic screams, quieted her straining lungs and sipped the last of her heartbeats, and let her drop.

Mrs. Warren stared incredulously at June's crumpled body and the horrible creature that blinked its lights and shifted its antennae questingly. With a muffled gasp, she sagged, knees and waist and neck, and fell soundlessly to the floor.

The refrigerator in the kitchen cleared its throat and the Eater turned from June with a *choonk* and slid away, crossing to the kitchen.

The Eater retracted its snout and slid back from the refrigerator. It lay quietly, its ears shifting from quarter to quarter.

The thermostat in the dining room clicked and the hot air furnace began to hum. The Eater slid to the wall under the register that was set just below the ceilings. Its snout extended and lifted and narrowed until the end of it slipped through one of the register openings. The furnace hum choked off abruptly and the snout end flipped back into sight.

Then there was quiet, deep and unbroken until the Eater tilted its ears and slid up to Mrs. Warren.

In such silence, even a pulse was noise.

There was a sound like a straw in the bottom of a soda glass.

A stillness was broken by the shrilling of a siren on the main highway four blocks away.

A *choonk* and a slither and the metallic bump of runners down the three front steps.

And a quiet, quiet house on a quiet side street. Hush.

The unconscious psyche of the child is truly limitless in extent and of incalculable age. The dreams of three- and four-year-old children . . . are so strikingly mythological and so fraught with meaning that one would take them at once for the dreams of grown-ups, if one did not know who the dreamer was. They are the last vestiges of a dwindling collective psyche which dreamingly reiterates the perennial contents of the human soul.

C.G. Jung, *The Development of Personality*

Man's need to understand the world and his experience in it symbolically as well as realistically may be noted early in the lives of many children. The symbolic, imaginative view of the world is just as organic a part of the child's life as the view transmitted by the sense organs. It represents a natural and spontaneous striving which adds to man's biological bond a parallel and equivalent psychic bond, thus enriching life by another dimension—and it is eminently this dimension that makes man what he is.

J. Jacobi, *Complex/Archetype/Symbol*

The magician is seated in his high chair and looks upon the world with favor. He is at the height of his powers. If he closes his eyes, he causes the world to disappear. If he opens his eyes, he causes the world to come back. If there is harmony within him, the world is harmonious. If rage shatters his inner harmony, the unity of the world is shattered. If desire arises within him, he utters the magic syllables that causes the desired object to appear. His wishes, his thoughts, his gestures, his noises command the universe.

The magician stands midway between two worlds, but the world he commands at eighteen months is already waiting to take away his magic, and he himself has begun to make certain observations which cast doubt upon his powers. Somewhere around the end of the first year he began to discover that he was not the initiator of all activity, that causes for certain events existed outside of himself, quite independent of his needs and his wishes, but now, in the middle of the second year, the magician makes a discovery which will slowly lead him to his downfall. The magician will be undone by his own magic. For when he ascends to the heights of word-magic, when he discovers he can command with a word, he will be lured into a new world, he will commit himself unknowingly to new laws of thinking, the principles of this second world which oppose magic by means of the word.

Selma H. Fraiberg, *The Magic Years*

Summer

John Ashbery

There is that sound like the wind
Forgetting in the branches that means something
Nobody can translate. And there is the sobering "later on,"
When you consider what a thing meant, and put it down.

For the time being the shadow is ample
And hardly seen, divided among the twigs of a tree,
The trees of a forest, just as life is divided up
Between you and me, and among all the others out there.

And the thinning-out phase follows
The period of reflection. And suddenly, to be dying
Is not a little or mean or cheap thing,
Only wearying, the heat unbearable,

And also the little mindless constructions put upon
Our fantasies of what we did: summer, the ball of pine needles,
The loose fates serving our acts, with token smiles,
Carrying out their instructions too accurately—

Too late to cancel them now—and winter, the twitter
Of cold stars at the pane, that describes with broad gestures
This state of being that is not so big after all.
Summer involves going down as a steep flight of steps

To a narrow ledge over the water. Is this it, then,
This iron comfort, these reasonable taboos,
Or did you mean it when you stopped? And the face
Resembles yours, the one reflected in the water.

Time One is the way I experience time when I am passive and unfocussed.

Time Two is the way I experience time when my mind becomes self-governing, which is what happens when it focusses on *meaning*.

Time Three is the way I experience time when the creative chain reaction begins, when I experience a sense of total control of my mental processes and unwavering perception of meaning.

J.B. Priestley, *Three Orders of Time*

In the imagination of man exist the seeds of all moral and scientific improvement; chemistry was first alchemy, and out of astrology sprang astronomy. In the childhood of those sciences the imagination opened a way, and furnished materials, on which the ratiocinative powers in a maturer stage operated with success. The imagination is the distinguishing characteristic of man as a progressive being . . .

William Walsh, *The Use of Imagination*

Reality Is an Activity of the Most August Imagination
Wallace Stevens

Last Friday, in the big light of last Friday night,
We drove home from Cornwall to Hartford, late.

It was not a night blown at a glassworks in Vienna
Or Venice, motionless, gathering time and dust.

There was a crush of strength in a grinding going round,
Under the front of the westward evening star,

The vigor of glory, a glittering in the veins,
As things emerged and moved and were dissolved,

Either in distance, change or nothingness,
The visible transformations of summer night,

An argentine abstraction approaching form
And suddenly denying itself away.

There was an insolid billowing of the solid.
Night's moonlight lake was neither water nor air.

Dwarf Trees
Joy Kogawa

Out of the many small embarrassments of the day
Grew a miniature personality
Leafing itself gingerly in whatever genuine smile
It recognized in the thick undergrowth.
Dwarf trees planted in a fertile gentleness
Beside lush vegetation and sheltering green fans
Grew angular and stunted in a constant adjustment to cutting.
Horns of new growths sprouted
To bleed into warts and tiny anxieties.
Glances of disapproval felt as sharply
As salivating fangs tore at limbs.
Men developed into twisted sculptures of endurance
Bowing and smiling in civilized anger
And old women pruned daily into careful beauty
Glanced away in a cultivated shyness
Hiding smiles with humpbacked hands
Symbolizing by small gestures
Tiny treasures from a hidden childhood.

The Hounds of Tindalos

Frank Belknap Long

"I'm glad you came," said Chalmers. He was sitting by the window and his face was very pale. Two tall candles guttered at his elbow and cast a sickly amber light over his long nose and slightly receding chin. Chalmers would have nothing modern about his apartment. He had the soul of a mediaeval ascetic, and he preferred illuminated manuscripts to automobiles, and leering stone gargoyles to radios and adding-machines.

As I crossed the room to the settee he had cleared for me I glanced at his desk and was surprised to discover that he had been studying the mathematical formulae of a celebrated contemporary physicist, and that he had covered many sheets of thin yellow paper with curious geometric designs.

"Einstein and John Dee are strange bedfellows," I said as my gaze wandered from his mathematical charts to the sixty or seventy quaint books that comprised his strange little library. Plotinus and Emanuel Moscopulus, St. Thomas Aquinas and Frenicle de Bessy stood elbow to elbow in the somber ebony bookcase, and chairs, table and desk were littered with pamphlets about mediaeval sorcery and witchcraft and black magic, and all of the valiant glamorous things that the modern world has repudiated.

Chalmers smiled engagingly, and passed me a Russian cigarette on a curiously carved tray. "We are just discovering now," he said, "that the old alchemists and sorcerers were two-thirds *right*, and that your modern biologist and materialist is nine-tenths *wrong*."

"You have always scoffed at modern science," I said, a little impatiently.

"Only at scientific dogmatism," he replied. "I have always been a rebel, a champion of originality and lost causes; that is why I have chosen to repudiate the conclusions of contemporary biologists."

"And Einstein?" I asked.

"A priest of transcendental mathematics!" he murmured reverently. "A profound mystic and explorer of the great *suspected*."

"Then you do not entirely despise science."

"Of course not," he affirmed. "I merely distrust the scientific positivism of the past fifty years, the positi-

vism of Haeckel and Darwin and of Mr. Bertrand Russell. I believe that biology has failed pitifully to explain the mystery of man's origin and destiny."

"Give them time," I retorted.

Chalmers' eyes glowed. "My friend," he murmured, "your pun is sublime. Give them *time*. That is precisely what I would do. But your modern biologist scoffs at time. He has the key but he refuses to use it. What do we know of time, really? Einstein believes that it is relative, that it can be interpreted in terms of space, of *curved* space. But must we stop there? When mathematics fails us can we not advance by—insight?"

"You are treading on dangerous ground," I replied. "That is a pitfall that your true investigator avoids. That is why modern science has advanced so slowly. It accepts nothing that it cannot demonstrate. But you—"

"I would take hashish, opium, all manner of drugs. I would emulate the sages of the East. And then perhaps I would apprehend—"

"What?"

"The fourth dimension."

"Theosophical rubbish!"

"Perhaps. But I believe that drugs expand human consciousness. William James agreed with me. And I have discovered a new one."

"A new drug?"

"It was used centuries ago by Chinese alchemists, but it is virtually unknown in the West. Its occult properties are amazing. With its aid and the aid of my mathematical knowledge I believe that I can *go back through time*."

"I do not understand."

"Time is merely our imperfect perception of a new dimension of space. Time and motion are both illusions. Everything that has existed from the beginning of the world *exists now*. Events that occurred centuries ago on this planet continue to exist in another dimension of space. Events that will occur centuries from now *exist already*. We cannot perceive their existence because we cannot enter the dimension of space that contains them. Human beings as we know them are merely fractions, infinitesimally small fractions of one enormous whole. Every human being is linked with *all* the life that has preceded him on this planet. All of his ancestors are parts of him. Only time separates him from his forebears, and time is an illusion and does not exist."

"I think I understand," I murmured.

"It will be sufficient for my purpose if you can form a vague idea of what I wish to achieve. I wish to strip from my eyes the veils of illusion that time has thrown over them, and see the *beginning and the end*."

"And you think this new drug will help you?"

"I am sure that it will. And I want you to help me. I intend to take the drug immediately. I cannot wait. I must *see*." His eyes glittered strangely. "I am going back, back through time."

He rose and strode to the mantel. When he faced me again he was holding a small square box in the palm of his hand. "I have here five pellets of the drug Liao. It was used by the Chinese philosopher Lao Tze, and while under its influence he visioned Tao. Tao is the most mysterious force in the world; it surrounds and pervades all things; it contains the visible universe and everything that we call reality. He who apprehends the mysteries of Tao sees clearly all that was and will be."

"What we want is *complete* imaginative experience which goes through the whole soul and body": the whole consciousness of men working together in unison and oneness: instinct, intuition, mind, intellect all fused into one complete consciousness, and grasping what we may call a complete truth, or a complete vision, a complete revelation . . . "

Phoenix

"Rubbish!" I retorted.

"Tao resembles a great animal, recumbent, motionless, containing in its enormous body all the worlds of our universe, the past, the present and the future. We see portions of this great monster through a slit, which we call time. With the aid of this drug I shall enlarge the slit. I shall behold the great figure of life, the great recumbent beast in its entirety."

"And what do you wish me to do?"

"Watch, my friend. Watch and take notes. And if I go back too far you must recall me to reality. You can recall me by shaking me violently. If I appear to be suffering acute physical pain you must recall me at once."

"Chalmers," I said, "I wish you wouldn't make this experiment. You are taking dreadful risks. I don't believe that there is any fourth dimension and I emphatically do not believe in Tao. And I don't

approve of your experimenting with unknown drugs."

"I know the properties of this drug," he replied. "I know precisely how it affects the human animal and I know its dangers. The risk does not reside in the drug itself. My only fear is that I may become lost in time. You see, I shall assist the drug. Before I swallow this pellet I shall give my undivided attention to the geometric and algebraic symbols that I have traced on this paper." He raised the mathematical chart that rested on his knee. "I shall prepare my mind for an excursion into time. I shall approach the fourth dimension with my conscious mind before I take the drug which will enable me to exercise occult powers of perception. Before I enter the dream world of the Eastern mystic I shall acquire all of the mathematical help that modern science can offer. This mathematical knowledge, this conscious approach to an actual apprehension of the fourth dimension of time will supplement the work of the drug. The drug will open up stupendous new vistas—the mathematical preparation will enable me to grasp them intellectually. I have often grasped the fourth dimension in dreams, emotionally, intuitively, but I have never been able to recall, in waking life, the occult splendors that were momentarily revealed to me.

"But with your aid, I believe that I can recall them. You will take down everything that I say while I am under the influence of the drug. No matter how strange or incoherent my speech may become you will omit nothing. When I awake I may be able to supply the key to whatever is mysterious or incredible. I am not sure that I shall succeed, but if I *do* succeed"—his eyes were strangely luminous—"*time will exist for me no longer!*"

He sat down abruptly. "I shall make the experiment at once. Please stand over there by the window and watch. Have you a fountain pen?"

I nodded gloomily and removed a pale green Waterman from my upper vest pocket.

"And a pad, Frank?"

I groaned and produced a memorandum book. "I emphatically disapprove of this experiment," I muttered. "You're taking a frightful risk."

"Don't be an asinine old woman!" he admonished. "Nothing that you can say will induce me to stop now. I entreat you to remain silent while I study these charts."

He raised the charts and studied them intently. I watched the clock on the mantel as it ticked out the seconds, and a curious dread clutched at my heart so that I choked.

Suddenly the clock stopped ticking, and exactly at that moment Chalmers swallowed the drug.

I rose quickly and moved toward him, but his eyes implored me not to interfere. "The clock has stopped," he murmured. "The forces that control it approve of my experiment. *Time* stopped, and I swallowed the drug. I pray God that I shall not lose my way."

He closed his eyes and leaned back on the sofa. All of the blood had left his face and he was breathing heavily. It was clear that the drug was acting with extraordinary rapidity.

"It is beginning to get dark," he murmured. "Write that. It is beginning to get dark and the familiar objects in the room are fading out. I can discern them vaguely through my eyelids, but they are fading swiftly."

I shook my pen to make the ink come and wrote rapidly in shorthand as he continued to dictate.

"I am leaving the room. The walls are vanishing and I can no longer see any of the familiar objects. Your face, though, is still visible to me. I hope that you are writing. I think that I am about to make a great leap—a leap through space. Or perhaps it is through time that I shall make the leap. I cannot tell. Everything is dark, indistinct."

Imagination is a communion of the soul and the external world (since from birth onward life is continuously shaped by nature, which penetrates one's being and influences one's thought).

June K. Singer, *The Unholy Bible*

He sat for a while silent, with his head sunk upon his breast. Then suddenly he stiffened and his eyelids fluttered open. "God in heaven!" he cried. "I see!"

He was straining forward in his chair, staring at the opposite wall. But I knew that he was looking beyond the wall and that the objects in the room no longer existed for him. "Chalmers," I cried, "Chalmers, shall I wake you?"

"Do not!" he shrieked. "*I see everything.* All of the billions of lives that preceded me on this planet are before me at this moment. I see men of all ages, all races, all colors. They are fighting, killing, building, dancing, singing. They are sitting about rude fires on lonely gray deserts, and flying through the air in monoplanes. They are riding the seas in bark canoes and enormous steamships; they are painting bison and mammoths on the walls of dismal caves and covering huge canvases with queer futuristic designs. I watch the migrations from Atlantis. I watch the migrations from Lemuria. I see the elder races—a strange horde of black dwarfs overwhelming Asia, and the Neandertalers with lowered heads and bent knees ranging obscenely across Europe. I watch the Achaeans streaming into the Greek islands, and the

---

Imagination creates shapes by which reality can be revealed.

C.M. Bowra, *The Romantic Imagination*

---

crude beginnings of Hellenic culture. I am in Athens and Pericles is young. I am standing on the soil of Italy. I assist in the rape of the Sabines; I march with the Imperial Legions. I tremble with awe and wonder as the enormous standards go by and the ground shakes with the tread of the victorious *hastati*. A thousand naked slaves grovel before me as I pass in a litter of gold and ivory drawn by night-black oxen from Thebes, and the flowergirls scream *'Ave Caesar'* as I nod and smile. I am myself a slave on a Moorish galley. I watch the erection of a great cathedral. Stone by stone it rises, and through months and years I stand and watch each stone as it falls into place. I am burned on a cross head downward in the thymescented gardens of Nero, and I watch with amusement and scorn the torturers at work in the chambers of the Inquisition.

"I walk in the holiest sanctuaries; I enter the temples of Venus. I kneel in adoration before the Magna Mater, and I throw coins on the bare knees of the sacred courtezans who sit with veiled faces in the groves of Babylon. I creep into an Elizabethan theater and with the stinking rabble about me I applaud *The Merchant of Venice*. I walk with Dante through the narrow streets of Florence. I meet the young Beatrice, and the hem of her garment brushes my sandals as I stare enraptured. I am a priest of Isis, and my magic astounds the nations. Simon Magus kneels before me, imploring my assistance, and Pharaoh trembles when I approach. In India I talk with the Masters and run screaming from their presence, for their revalations are as salt on wounds that bleed.

"I perceive everything *simultaneously*. I perceive everything from all sides; I am a part of all the teeming billions about me. I exist in all men and all men exist in me. I perceive the whole of human history in a single instant, the past and the present.

"By simply *straining* I can see farther and farther back. Now I am going back through strange curves and angles. Angles and curves multiply about me. I perceive great segments of time through *curves*. There is *curved time*, and *angular time*. The beings that exist in angular time cannot enter curved time. It is very strange.

"I am going back and back. Man has disappeared from the earth. Gigantic reptiles crouch beneath enormous palms and swim through the loathly black waters of dismal lakes. Now the reptiles have disappeared. No animals remain upon the land, but beneath the waters, plainly visible to me, dark forms move slowly over the rotting vegetation.

"The forms are becoming simpler and simpler. Now they are single cells. All about me there are angles—strange angles that have no counterparts on the earth. I am desperately afraid.

"There is an abyss of being which man has never fathomed."

I stared. Chalmer had risen to his feet and he was gesticulating helplessly with his arms. "I am passing through unearthly angles; I am approaching—oh, the burning horror of it."

"Chalmers!" I cried. "Do you wish me to interfere?"

He brought his right hand quickly before his face, as though to shut out a vision unspeakable. "Not yet!" he cried; "I will go on. I will see—what—lies—beyond—"

A cold sweat streamed from his forehead and his shoulders jerked spasmodically. "Beyond life there are"—his face grew ashen with terror—"*things* that I cannot distinguish. They move slowly through angles. They have no bodies, and they move slowly through outrageous angles."

It was then that I became aware of the odor in the room. It was a pungent, indescribable odor, so nauseous that I could scarcely endure it. I stepped quickly to the window and threw it open. When I returned to Chalmers and looked into his eyes I nearly fainted.

"I think they have scented me!" he shrieked. "They are slowly turning toward me."

He was trembling horribly. For a moment he clawed at the air with his hands. Then his legs gave way beneath him and he fell forward on his face, slobbering and moaning.

I watched him in silence as he dragged himself across the floor. He was no longer a man. His teeth were bared and saliva dripped from the corners of his mouth.

"Chalmers," I cried. "Chalmers, stop it! Stop it, do you hear?"

As if in reply to my appeal he commenced to utter hoarse convulsive sounds which resembled nothing so much as the barking of a dog, and began a sort of hideous writhing in a circle about the room. I bent and seized him by the shoulders. Violently, desperately, I shook him. He turned his head and snapped at my wrist. I was sick with horror, but I dared not release him for fear that he would destroy himself in a paroxysm of rage.

"Chalmers," I muttered, "you must stop that. There is nothing in this room that can harm you. Do you understand?"

The images which appear in the nearer reaches of the collective sub-conscious have meaning in relation to the basic facts of human experience; but here, at the limits of the visionary world, we are confronted by facts which, like the facts of external nature, are independent of man, both individually and collectively, and exist in their own right. And their meaning consists precisely in this, that they are intensely themselves and, being intensely themselves, are manifestations of the essential givenness, the non-human otherness of the universe.

Aldous Huxley, *The Doors of Perception*

I continued to shake and admonish him, and gradually the madness died out of his face. Shivering convulsively, he crumpled into a grotesque heap on the Chinese rug.

I carried him to the sofa and deposited him upon it. His features were twisted in pain, and I knew that he was still struggling dumbly to escape from abominable memories.

"Whisky," he muttered. "You'll find a flask in the cabinet by the window—upper left-hand drawer."

When I handed him the flask his fingers tightened about it until the knuckles showed blue. "They nearly got me," he gasped. He drained the stimulant in immoderate gulps, and gradually the color crept back into his face.

"That drug was the very devil!" I murmured.

"It wasn't the drug," he moaned.

His eyes no longer glared insanely, but he still wore the look of a lost soul.

"They scented me in time," he moaned. "I went too far."

"What were *they* like?" I said, to humor him.

He leaned forward and gripped my arm. He was shivering horribly. "No words in our language can describe them!" He spoke in a hoarse whisper. "They are symbolized vaguely in the myth of the Fall, and in an obscene form which is occasionally found engraved on ancient tablets. The Greeks had a name for them, which veiled their essential foulness. The tree, the snake, and the apple—these are the vague symbols of a most awful mystery."

His voice had risen to a scream. "Frank, Frank, a terrible and unspeakable *deed* was done in the beginning. Before time, the *deed*, and from the deed—"

He had risen and was hysterically pacing the room. "The deeds of the dead move through angles in dim recesses of time. They are hungry and athirst!"

"Chalmers," I pleaded to quiet him. "We are living in the third decade of the Twentieth Century."

"They are lean and athirst!" he shrieked. *"The Hounds of Tindalos!"*

"Chalmers, shall I phone for a physician?"

"A physician cannot help me now. They are horrors of the soul, and yet"—he hid his face in his hands and groaned—"they are real, Frank. I saw them for a ghastly moment. For a moment I stood on the *other side*. I stood on the pale gray shores beyond time and space. In an awful light that was not light, in a silence that shrieked, I saw *them*.

"All the evil in the universe was concentrated in their lean, hungry bodies. Or had they bodies? I saw them only for a moment; I cannot be certain. *But I heard them breathe.* Indescribable for a moment I felt their breath upon my face. They turned toward me and I fled screaming. In a single moment I fled screaming through time. I fled down quintillions of years.

"But they scented me. Men awake in them cosmic hungers. We have escaped, momentarily, from the foulness that rings them round. They thirst for that in us which is clean, which is clean, which emerged from the deed without stain. There is a part of us which did not partake in the deed, and that they hate. But do not imagine that they are literally, prosaically evil. They are beyond good and evil as we know it. They are that which in the beginning fell away from cleanliness. Through the deed they became bodies of death, receptacles of all foulness. But they are not evil in *our* sense because in the spheres through which they move there is no thought, no moral, no right or wrong as we understand it. There is merely the pure and the foul. The foul expresses itself through angle; the pure through curves. Man, the pure part of him, is descended from a curve. Do not laugh. I mean that literally."

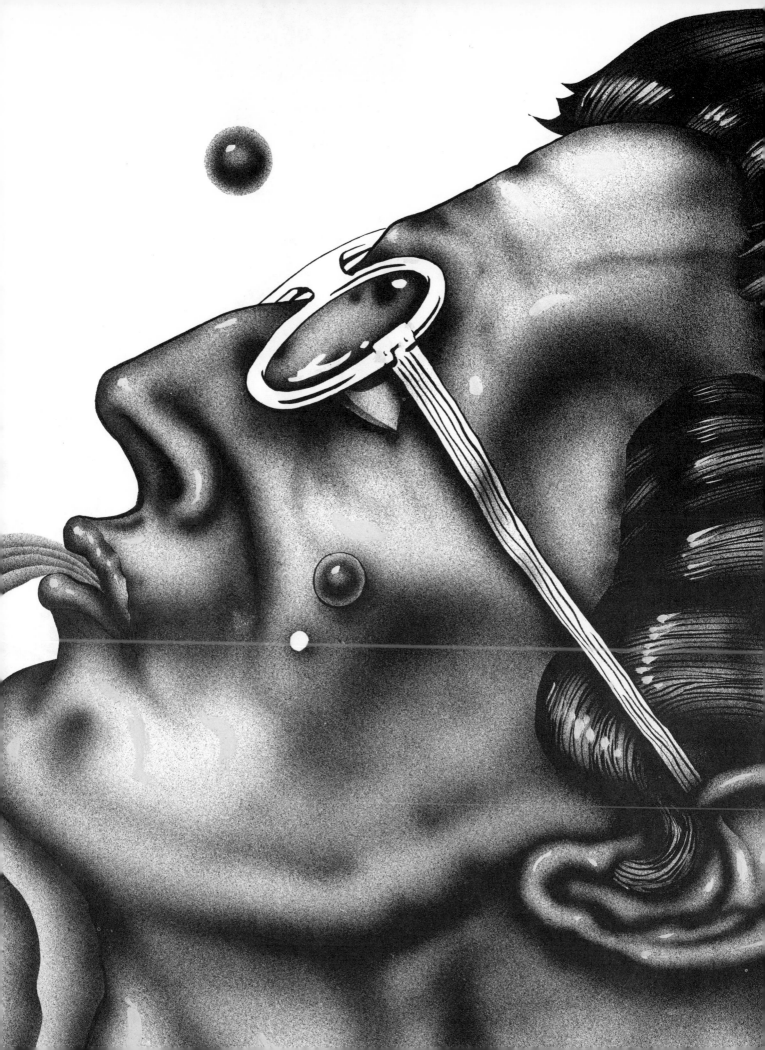

I rose and searched for my hat. "I'm dreadfully sorry for you, Chalmers," I said, as I walked toward the door. "But I don't intend to stay and listen to such gibberish. I'll send my physician to see you. He's an elderly, kindly chap and he won't be offended if you tell him to go to the devil. But I hope you'll respect his advice. A week's rest in a good sanitarium should benefit you immeasurably."

I heard him laughing as I descended the stairs, but his laughter was so utterly mirthless that it moved me to tears.

2

When Chalmers phoned the following morning my first impulse was to hang up the receiver immediately. His request was so unusual and his voice was so wildly hysterical that I feared any further association with him would result in the impairment of my own sanity. But I could not doubt the genuineness of his misery, and when he broke down completely and I heard him sobbing over the wire I decided to comply with his request.

"Very well," I said. "I will come over immediately and bring the plaster."

En route to Chalmers' home I stopped at a hardware store and purchased twenty pounds of plaster of Paris. When I entered my friend's room he was crouching by the window watching the opposite wall out of eyes that were feverish with fright. When he saw me he rose and seized the parcel containing the plaster with an avidity that amazed and horrified me. He had extruded all of the furniture and the room presented a desolate appearance.

"It is just conceivable that we can thwart them!" he exclaimed. "But we must work rapidly. Frank, there is a stepladder in the hall. Bring it here immediately. And then fetch a pail of water."

"What for?" I murmured.

He turned sharply and there was a flush on his face. "To mix the plaster, you fool!" he cried. "To mix the plaster that will save our bodies and souls from a contamination unmentionable. To mix the plaster that will save the world from—Frank, *they must be kept out!*"

"Who?" I murmured.

"The Hounds of Tindalos!" he muttered. "They can only reach us through angles. We must eliminate all angles from this room. I shall plaster up all of the corners, all of the crevices. We must make this room resemble the interior of a sphere."

I knew that it would have been useless to argue with him. I fetched the stepladder, Chalmers mixed the plaster, and for three hours we labored. We filled in the four corners of the wall and the intersections of the floor and wall and the wall and ceiling, and we rounded the sharp angles of the window-seat.

"I shall remain in this room until they return in time," he affirmed when our task was completed. "When they discover that the scent leads through curves they will return. They will return ravenous and snarling and unsatisfied to the foulness that was in the beginning, before time, beyond space."

He nodded graciously and lit a cigarette. "It was good of you to help," he said.

"Will you not see a physician, Chalmers?" I pleaded.

"Perhaps—tomorrow," he murmured. "But now I must watch and wait."

"Wait for what?" I urged.

Chalmers smiled wanly. "I know that you think me insane," he said. "You have a shrewd but prosaic mind, and you cannot conceive of an entity that does not depend for its existence on force and matter. But did it ever occur to you, my friend, that force and matter are merely the barriers, to perception imposed by time and space? When one knows, as I do, that time and space are identical and that they are both deceptive because they are merely imperfect manifestations of a higher reality, one no longer seeks in the visible world for an explanation of the mystery and terror of being."

I rose and walked toward the door.

"Forgive me," he cried. "I did not mean to offend you. You have a superlative intellect, but I—I have a *superhuman* one. It is only natural that I should be aware of your limitations."

"Phone if you need me," I said, and descended the stairs two steps at a time. "I'll send my physician over at once," I muttered, to myself. "He's a hopeless maniac, and heaven knows what will happen if someone doesn't take a charge of him immediately."

3

The following is a condensation of two announcements which appeared in the Partridgeville Gazette *for July 3, 1928:*

Earthquake Shakes Financial District

At 2 o'clock this morning an earth tremor of unusual severity broke several plate-glass windows in Central Square and completely disorganized the electric and street railway systems. The tremor was felt in the outlying districts and the steeple of the First Baptist Church on Angell Hill (designed by Christopher Wren in 1717) was entirely demolished. Firemen are now attempting to put out a blaze which threatens to destroy the Partridgeville Glue Works. An investigation is promised by the mayor and an immediate attempt will be made to fix responsibility for this disastrous occurrence.

OCCULT WRITER MURDERED
BY UNKNOWN GUEST

Horrible Crime in Central Square

Mystery Surrounds Death of Halpin Chalmers

At 9 A.M. today the body of Halpin Chalmers, author and journalist, was found in an empty room above the jewelry store of Smithwich and Isaacs, 24 Central Square. The coroner's investigation revealed that the room had been rented furnished to Mr. Chalmers on May 1, and that he had himself disposed of the furniture a fortnight ago. Chalmers was the author of several recondite books on occult themes, and a member of the Bibliographic Guild. He formerly resided in Brooklyn, New York.

At 7 A.M. Mr. L.E. Hancock, who occupies the apartment opposite Chalmers' room in the Smithwick and Isaacs establishment, smelt a peculiar odor when he opened his door to take in his cat and the morning edition of the *Partridgeville Gazette*. The odor he describes as extremely acrid and nauseous, and he affirms that it was so strong in the vicinity of Chalmer's room that he was obliged to hold his nose when he approached that section of the hall.

He was about to return to his own apartment when it occurred to him that Chalmers might have accidentally forgotten to turn off the gas in his kitchenette. Becoming considerably alarmed at the thought, he decided to investigate, and when repeated tappings on Chalmers' door brought no response he notified the superintendent. The latter opened the door by means of a pass key, and the two men quickly made their way into Chalmers' room. The room was utterly destitute of furniture, and Hancock asserts that when he first glanced at the floor his heart went cold within him, and that the superintendent, without saying a word, walked to the open window and stared at the building opposite for fully five minutes.

Chalmers lay stretched upon his back in the center of the room. He was starkly nude, and his chest and arms were covered with a peculiar bluish pus or ichor. His head lay grotesquely upon his chest. It had been completely severed from his body, and the features were twisted and torn and horribly mangled. Nowhere was there a trace of blood.

The room presented a most astonishing appearance. The intersections of the walls, ceiling and floor had been thickly smeared with plaster of Paris, but at intervals fragments had cracked and fallen off, and someone had grouped these upon the floor about the murdered man so as to form a perfect triangle.

Beside the body were several sheets of charred yellow paper. These bore fantastic geometric designs and symbols and several hastily scrawled sentences. The sentences were almost illegible and so absurd in context that they furnished no possible clue to the perpetrator of the crime. "I am waiting and watching," Chalmers wrote. "I sit by the window and watch walls and ceiling. I do not believe they can reach me, but I must beware of the Doels. Perhaps *they* can help them break through. The satyrs will help, and they can advance through the scarlet circles. The Greeks knew a way of preventing that. It is a great pity that we have forgotten so much."

On another sheet of paper, the most badly charred of the seven or eight fragments found by Detective Sergeant Douglas (of the Partridgeville Reserve), was scrawled the following:

"Good God, the plaster is falling! A terrific shock has loosened the plaster and it is falling. An earthquake perhaps! I never could have anticipated this. It is growing dark in the room. I must phone Frank. But can he get here in time? I will try. I will recite the Einstein formula. I will—God, they are breaking through! They are breaking through! Smoke is pouring from the corners of the wall. Their tongues—ahhhh—"

In the opinion of Detective Sergeant Douglas, Chalmers was poisoned by some obscure chemical. He has sent specimens of the strange blue slime found on Chalmers' body to the Partridgeville Chemical Laboratories; and he expects the report will shed new light on one of the most mysterious crimes of recent years. That Chalmers entertained a guest on the evening preceeding the earthquake is certain, for his neighbor distinctly heard a low murmur of conversation in the former's room as he passed it on his way to the stairs. Suspicion points strongly to this unknown visitor and the police are diligently endeavoring to discover his identity.

4

Report of James Morton, chemist and bacteriologist:
   My dear Mr. Douglas:

The fluid sent to me for analysis is the most peculiar that I have ever examined. It resembles living protoplasm, but it lacks the peculiar substances known as enzymes. Enzymes catalyze the chemical reactions occurring in living cells, and when the cell dies they cause it to disintegrate by hydrolyzation. Without enzymes protoplasm should possess enduring vitality, i.e., immortality. Enzymes are the negative components, so to speak, of unicellular organism, which is the basis of all life. That living matter can exist without enzymes biologists emphatically deny. And yet the substance that you have sent me is alive and it lacks these "indispensable" bodies. Good God, sir, do you realize what astounding new vistas this opens up?

5

Excerpt from The Secret Watcher *by the late Halpin Chalmers:*

What if, parallel to the life we know, there is another life that does not die, which lacks the elements that destroy *our* life? Perhaps in another dimension there is a *different* force from that which generates our life. Perhaps this force emits energy, or something similar to energy, which passes from the unknown dimension where *it* is and creates a new form of cell life in our dimension. No one knows that such new cell life does exist in our dimension. Ah, but I have seen *its* manifestations. I have *talked* with them. In my room at night I have talked with the Doels. And in dreams I have seen their maker. I have stood on the dim shore beyond time and matter and seen *it*. It moves through strange curves and outrageous angles. Some day I shall travel in time and meet *it* face to face.

Perhaps there do indeed exist universes interpenetrating with ours; perhaps of a high complexity; perhaps containing their own forms of awareness; constructed out of other particles and other interactions than those we know now, but awaiting discovery through some common but elusive interactions that we have yet to spot. It is not the physicist's job to make this sort of speculation, but today, when we are so much less sure of the natural world than we were two decades ago, he can at least license it.

Denys Wilkinson

The Crazed Moon
W.B. Yeats

Crazed through much child-bearing
The moon is staggering in the sky;
Moon-struck by the despairing
Glances of her wandering eye
We grope, and grope in vain,
For children born of her pain.

Children dazed or dead!
When she in all her virginal pride
First trod on the mountain's head
What stir ran through the countryside
Where every foot obeyed her glance!
What manhood led the dance!

Fly-catchers of the moon,
Our hands are blenched, our fingers seem
But slender needles of bone;
Blenched by that malicious dream
They are spread wide that each
May rend what comes in reach.

There is really nothing more to say when we come back
to that beginning of all beginnings that is nothing at all.
Only when you begin to lose that Alpha and Omega do
you want to start to talk and to write, and then there is
no end to it, words, words, words. At best and most they
are perhaps *in memoriam*, evocations, conjurations,
incantations, emanations, shimmering, iridescent flares
in the sky of darkness, a just still feasible tact, indiscre-
tions, perhaps forgivable . . .

City lights at night, from the air, receding, like these
words, atoms each containing its own world and every
other world. Each a fuse to set you off . . .

If I could turn you on, if I could drive you out of your
wretched mind, if I could tell you I would let you know.

R.D. Laing, *The Bird of Paradise*

Voices of Earth
Archibald Lampman

We have not heard the music of the spheres,
The song of star to star, but there are sounds
More deep than human joy and human tears,
That Nature uses in her common rounds;
The fall of streams, the cry of winds that strain
The oak, the roaring of the sea's surge, might
Of thunder breaking afar off, or rain
That falls by minutes in the summer night.
These are the voices of earth's secret soul,
Uttering the mystery from which she came.
To him who hears them grief beyond control,
Or joy inscrutable without a name,
Wakes in his heart thoughts bedded there,
    impearled,
Before the birth and making of the world.

Every transformation or creative process comprises stages of possession. To be moved, captivated, spellbound, signify to be possessed by something; and without such a fascination and the emotional tension connected with it, no concentration, no lasting interest, no creative process, are possible. Every possession can justifiably be interpreted either as a one-sided narrowing or as an intensification and deepening. The exclusivity and radicality of such "possession" represent both an opportunity and a danger. But no great achievement is possible if one does not accept this risk.

Erich Neumann, *Art and the Creative Unconscious*

Storm
Jay Macpherson

That strong creature   from before the Flood,
headless, sightless,   without bone or blood,
a wandering voice,   a travelling spirit,
butting to be born,   fierce to inherit
acreage of pity,   the world of love,
the Christian child's kingdom,   and remove
the tall towered gates   where the proud sea lay
crouched on its paws   in the first day—
came chaos again,   that outsider
would ride in,   blind steed, blind rider:
till then wails at windows,   denies relief,
batters the body   in speechless grief,
thuds in the veins,   crumples in the bone,
wrestles in darkness   and alone
for kingdoms cold,   for salt, sand, stone,
forever dispossessed.
              Who raised this beast,
this faceless angel,   shall give him rest.

The World Voice
Bliss Carman

I heard the summer sea
Murmuring to the shore
Some endless story of a wrong
The whole world must deplore.

I heard the mountain wind
Conversing with the trees
Of an old sorrow of the hills
Mysterious as the sea's.

And all that haunted day
It seemed that I could hear
The echo of an ancient speech
Ring in my listening ear.

And then it came to me,
That all that I had heard
Was my own heart in the sea's voice
And the wind's lonely word.

from **A Voyage to Arcturus**
David Lindsay

He climbed into the embrasure. His feelings translated themselves into vision, and he saw a sight that caused him to turn pale. A gigantic, self-luminous sphere was hanging in the sky, occupying nearly the whole of it. This sphere was composed entirely of two kinds of active beings. There were a myriad of tiny green corpuscles, varying in size from the very small to the almost indiscernible. They were not green, but he somehow saw them so. They were all striving in one direction–toward himself, toward Muspel, but were too feeble and miniature to make any headway. Their action produced the marching rhythm he had previously felt, but this rhythm was not intrinsic in the corpuscles themselves, but was a consequence of the obstruction they met with. And, surrounding these

atoms of life and light, were far larger whirls of white light that gyrated hither and thither, carrying the green corpuscles with them wherever they desired. Their whirling motion was accompanied by the waltzing rhythm. It seemed to Nightspore that the green atoms were not only being danced about against their will but were suffering excruciating shame and degradation in consequence. The larger ones were steadier than the extremely small, a few were even almost stationary, and one was advancing in the direction it wished to go.

He turned his back to the window, buried his face in his hands, and searched in the dim recesses of his memory for an explanation of what he had just seen. Nothing came straight, but horror and wrath began to take possession of him.

On his way upward to the next window, invisible fingers seemed to him to be squeezing his heart and twisting it about here and there; but he never dreamed

of turning back. His mood was so grim that he did not once permit himself to pause. Such was his physical distress by the time that he had clambered into the recess, that for several minutes he could see nothing at all—the world seemed to be spinning round him rapidly.

When at last he looked, he saw the same sphere as before, but now all was changed on it. It was a world of rocks, minerals, water, plants, animals, and men. He saw the whole world at one view, yet everything was so magnified that he could distinguish the smallest details of life. In the interior of every individual, of every aggregate of individuals, of every chemical atom, he clearly perceived the presence of the green corpuscles. But, according to the degree of dignity of the life form, they were fragmentary or comparatively large. In the crystal, for example, the green, imprisoned life was so minute as to be scarcely visible; in some men it was hardly bigger; but in other men and women it was twenty or a hundred times greater. But, great or small, it played an important part in every individual. It appeared as if the whirls of white light, which *were* the individuals, and plainly showed themselves beneath the enveloping bodies, were delighted with existence and wished only to enjoy it, but the green corpuscles were in a condition of eternal discontent, yet, blind and not knowing which way to turn for liberation, kept changing form, as though breaking a new path, by way of experiment. Whenever the old grotesque became metamorphosed into the new grotesque, it was in every case the direct work of the green atoms, trying to escape toward Muspel, but encountering immediate opposition. These subdivided sparks of living, fiery spirit were hopelessly imprisoned in a ghastly mush of soft pleasure. They were being effeminated and corrupted—that is to say, *absorbed* in the foul, sickly enveloping forms.

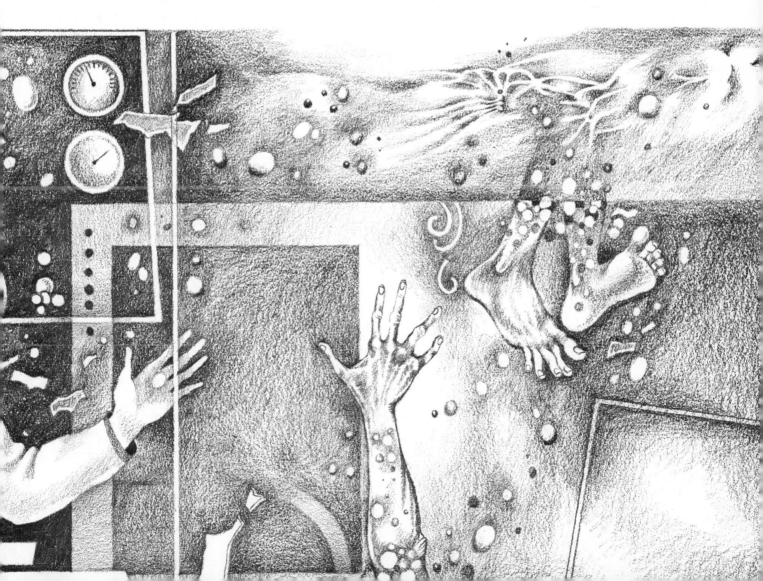

from The Ship of Ishtar

A. Merritt

Kenton lay listening to a soft whispering; persistent, continuous. It was like the breaking crests of little waves. The sound was all about him; a rippling susurration growing steadily more insistent. A light beat through his closed lids. He felt motion beneath him, a gentle cradling lift and fall. He opened his eyes.

He was on a ship, on a narrow deck, his head against the bulwarks. Before him was a mast rising out of a pit. Inside the pit he caught a glimpse of men straining at great oars. The mast seemed to be of wood covered with translucent, emerald lacquer. It stirred reluctant memories.

Where had he seen such a mast before?

His gaze crept up the shining shaft. There was a wide sail; a sail made of silk of opal, and bellying in the breath of a scented breeze. Low overhead hung a sky that was all a soft mist of silver.

Kenton heard a girl's voice, low and sweet. He sat up, dizzily. At his right he saw a templed cabin nestling under the curved tip of a sickled prow; it gleamed rosily. A balcony ran around it. Small trees blossomed on that balcony; while birds with feet and bills crimson as though dipped in wine of rubies flew and fluttered among the branches.

And suddenly he remembered the block from Babylon—the ship of enchantment he had freed from it. Swift upon that memory came realization, staggering, incredible.

He was on that ship—the Ship of Ishtar!

The girl's voice sounded again; was answered by a deep-toned golden other, in whose liquidly throaty notes was vibrant a debonair imperiousness. His gaze coursed along that trail of golden sound, leaped over the three women kneeling at its source; it fastened upon one face and hung there.

Never had he beheld such a woman!

Tall, willow-lithe, flame-slender she stood, staring beyond him. Her wide eyes beneath straight, daintily fine black brows were green as shoals of tropic seas, of depths of forest glens. Like sea and woods, they were filled with drifting, mysterious shadows. Her head was small; the features fine; the red mouth delicately amorous. In the hollow of her throat a dimple lay; a chalice for kisses; empty of them and eager to be filled.

Above her brows a silver crescent was set, slim as a newborn moon. Over each horn of the crescent poured a flood of red-gold hair, framing the lovely face, streaming down over high, bare breasts, falling in ringlets almost to sandaled feet. Pale pearls and rosy gems gleamed in those red-gold waves like jeweled drops of dew.

Were she maid or woman, Kenton could not tell. As young as spring she seemed—yet wise as autumn; Primavera of some archaic Botticelli—but Mona Lisa, too. If virginal in body, certainly not in soul.

He followed her mocking gaze. It led him to the door of the black cabin, where stood a man. Taller by a head than Kenton, massively built, his pale gray eyes stared unwinkingly upon the woman, somberly menacing, impassively malignant. His face was beardless, pallid, heavy and cruel. Despite his bulk his pose was snakelike; and in the pale eyes serpent and wolf were mated. His huge and flattened head was shaven; his great nose vulture-beaked; and from his shoulders black robes fell, shrouding him to his feet.

Behind him were three others, with shaven heads. Two were as still as he, and as deadly; each of the twain held a brazen, conch-shaped horn.

On the third Kenton's eyes lingered, fascinated. His pointed chin rested on a tall drum whose curved sides glistened with the diamonded skin of the royal python. He squatted, huge torso bare, knotted and gnarled, prodigiously powerful. His apelike arms were wound around the barreled tambour; spiderlike were the long fingers standing upon their tips on the drum head.

But it was the face that held Kenton. Sardonic, malicious—there was in it none of that evil concentrate in the others. The wide slit of his mouth was froglike; humor was on the thin lips. His deep-set, twinkling-black eyes dwelt upon the woman with frank admiration. From the lobes of his outstanding ears hung disks of jet.

Kenton felt a quick glow of friendliness for this squatting incarnation of satyr ugliness.

The woman paced swiftly down toward Kenton. When she halted he could have reached out a hand and touched her. Yet she did not seem to see him! Indeed, this was part of the strangeness of his first adventure upon the ship—that none heeded him; gave no hint of knowledge that he was there.

"Ho—Klaneth!" she cried. "Ho—Worm of Pestilence! I hear the voice of Ishtar! She is drawing near! Are you ready to do her homage, Worm of Nergal?"

A flicker of hate passed over the pallid face, like a little wave from hell.

"The House of the Goddess brims with light, Sharane," the man answered with a voice thick and dead and in some way foul. "But tell me, temple drab—does not my Dread Lord's shadow thicken behind me?"

Now Kenton saw that from the rosy temple a light was pulsing, stronger and ever stronger like a waxing moon within gigantic pearl; while down upon the black cabin gloom was gathering like a storm cloud!

"Yea!" mocked the woman. "The goddess comes! And your Dark Lord speeds to meet her! But why should that make you rejoice? For lo—she gives me clean strength ten thousandfold! And what are you, Klaneth, but a drain through which pours that filth you worship as Nergal!"

Now at this the two priests with the horns thrust themselves forward, gesturing, howling imprecations at the woman. The pale, cruel face of Klaneth grew grayer still and writhed with hate; he raised clenched hands, and from his mouth, flecked with foam, came a dreadful hissing.

A sudden wind smote the ship, like an opened hand, heeling it. From the doves burst a tumult of cries; they flew up like a little white cloud flecked with crimson; they fluttered around the woman. Three quick, backward steps she took.

The apelike arms of the frog-mouth drummer unwrapped, his spidery fingers poised over the head of the snake drum. The blackness deepened about him; hid him; cloaked all the ship's stern.

Kenton felt vast presences seize the ship—felt the gathering of fearful, unknown forces. He slid down on his haunches, pressed himself against the bulwarks. From the ivory deck blared a golden trumpeting; defiant; inhuman. Kenton turned his head, and on it the hair lifted and prickled.

Where the woman had been was now—no woman!

Resting on the rosy cabin was a great orb, an orb like the moon at full; but not like the moon, white and cold—an orb alive with pulsing roseate candescence. Out over the ship it poured its living, rosy rays and, bathed in them, the woman loomed—gigantic. The lids of the glorious eyes were closed. Yet through those closed lids eyes glared! Plainly he saw them—eyes hard as jade, white-hot with wrath, glaring through the closed lids as though those lids had been gossamer!

And the slender crescent upon the woman's brows was radiant now as the young moon itself; and all about it the masses of red-gold hair beat and tossed, streaming like rack of racing storm, swirling like silken pennons in whirlwind of war. Round and round the shining crescent whirled the cloud of the doves; snowy wings beating, red beaks open; screaming.

Out of the blackness roared the thunder of the serpent drum.

"Ai-ai-i!" From the moon-crowned shape came a cry like the jubilant clamor of newly wakened winds of spring shouting over pine-crested billows of a thousand hills. Answering it, another roaring of the drum; sustained and menacing. The blackness thinned. A face stared out, half veiled; bodiless, floating in the shadow. It was the face of Klaneth—and yet no more his face than that which challenged it was the woman Sharane's. The pale eyes had become twin pools of white hell flames; pupilless. On his brow sat throned the ageless, ultimate evil. For a heart beat the face hovered, framed by the darkness. Then the shadow dropped over it; hid it.

Now Kenton saw that this shadow hung like a curtain at the line where black deck met ivory deck, and that he lay upon the latter hardly a yard distant from where that line cut the ship in twain. He saw, too, that the radiance from the orb struck against this curtain, and made upon it a great circle that was like a web of beams spun from the rays of a rosy moon; and that against this shining web the shadow pressed, striving to break through.

And suddenly from the black deck the thunder of the serpent drum redoubled; the brazen conches shrieked. Drum thunder and shrieking horn blasts mingled and became one—the pulse of Abaddon, Lair of the Damned, throbbing in the voice of the Abyss. They fed the shadow, strengthened it; they were the rhythm of its will. Blacker, denser now, the shadow thrust against the web of light.

From Sharane's women, crouching low, shot storm of harpings, arpeggios like gusts of tiny arrows, and with them pipings from the double flutes that flew like shrill, swift javelins. Arrows and javelins of sound cut through the thunder hammer of the drum, the bellow of the horns; weakening them; beating them back.

A movement began within the shadow. It seethed. It—spawned!

Over all the face of the weblike disk of radiance black shapes swarmed. Their bodies were like monstrous larvae, slug-shaped, faceless. They tore at the web with black talons, strove to thrust through it with hideous tentacles, flailed it with batlike wings.

The web gave!

Its edge held firm, but slowly, slowly, the center was pushed back until the disk was like the half of a huge, hollow sphere. Within that hollow crawled and writhed and struck the monstrous shapes.

From the hidden deck drum and brazen horns roared triumph!

Again rang the golden trumpet cry of the woman. Out of the orb poised upon the cabin streamed an incandescence intolerable. The edges of the radiant web shot forward, curved—and closed upon the black spawn. Within it they milled and struggled like fish in a net.

And like a net lifted by some mighty hand the closed web was swung up high above the ship with all its infernal burden. Its brightness grew to match that of the great orb, whose rays were now piercing the darkness at the stern; putting it to rout. Within it the shapes of blackness squirmed, shrank; dissolved! From then came a faint, high-pitched, obscene wailing.

They were gone!

The globular net that had been the shining web opened. Out of it drifted a little cloud of ebon dust!

The web hovered; streamed back to the orb that had sent it forth.

Then, swiftly, the orb—was gone!

Gone, too, was the darkness that had shrouded the deck of Klaneth!

High above the ship the doves of Ishtar wheeled in a vast ring, crying victory.

A hand touched Kenton's shoulder. He looked up—straight into the shadowy eyes of the woman called Sharane: no goddess now, but only lovely, alluring woman. In those eyes he read amazement, startled disbelief. He felt the delicious warmth of her; inhaled her fragrance.

Kenton sprang to his feet. Too late he remembered the blow that had ended his fall upon the ship. A thrust of blinding pain shot through his head. The deck whirled round him. He tried to master the giddiness; he could not. Dizzily the ship spun beneath his feet; and beyond in wider arcs spun turquoise sea and silver horizon.

Now they formed a vortex, a maelstrom, down whose pit he was dropping—faster, ever faster. Around him was a formless blur; again he heard the tumult of the tempests, the shrillings of the winds of space. He abandoned himself to headlong, prodigious flight.

The winds died away. He was standing, his flight over, on solidity once more. He heard three clear bell notes. He opened tight-closed eyes.

Kenton stood within his own room!

There by the window glimmered the jeweled ship.

The bell he had heard had been his clock, chiming

the hour of six. Six o'clock! The last sound of his familiar world before the mystic sea had swept that world from under him had been the third stroke of that same hour, clipped off in mid-note. Why then—all he had seen, all his adventure, must have happened in half a clock chime!

Adventure? Had it been that? Or only a dream?

He lifted a hand and winced as it touched a throbbing bruise over his right temple. Well—that blow had been no dream! He stumbled over to the ship. He stared at it, incredulous. Then one by one he pulled at each of the manikins, each toy. Immovable, gemhard, part of the deck itself each seemed to be as each had been before.

And yet—In half a clock chime those toys had moved, new toys appeared!

For now the long-armed beater of the serpent drum stood upright on the black deck, peering toward the platform at the right of the mast, one hand pointing, the other resting on the shoulder of a manikin in glittering mail.

Nor was there any woman at the rosy cabin's door as there had been when he had loosed the mystery from the block. Clustered around the threshold were five slim girl toys with javelin in hands.

And the woman was on the starboard platform, bent low beside the rail as though looking at some one lying there.

Looking where he had crouched while over him had waged the battle between the radiant orb and core of blackness!

And the ship's oars were no longer buried in the turquoise waves—they were lifted, poised for a downward stroke!

Imagination makes man's world. This is not to say that his world is a fantasy, his life a dream, or any such poetic pseudo-philosophical thing. It means that his "world" is bigger than the stimuli which surrounds him, and the measure of it is the reach of his coherent and steady imagination. An animal's environment consists of the things that act on his senses. . . . his "world" has a fragmentary, intermittent existence, arising and collapsing with his activities. A human being's world hangs together, its events fit into each other; no matter how devious their connections, there always are connections, in one big framework of space and time. . . . An animal's environment is not really a "world", let alone "the world". . . . *The world* is something human.

Susanne K. Langer, *Philosophical Sketches*

The Cold Green Element
Irving Layton

At the end of the garden walk
the wind and its satellite wait for me;
their meaning I will not know
       until I go there,
but the black-hatted undertaker

who, passing, saw my heart beating in the grass,
is also going there. Hi, I tell him,
a great squall in the Pacific blew a dead poet
       out of the water,
who now hangs from the city's gates.

Crowds depart daily to see it, and return
with grimaces and incomprehension;
if its limbs twitched in the air
       they would sit at its feet
peeling their oranges.

And turning over I embrace like a lover
the trunk of a tree, one of those
for whom the lightning was too much
       and grew a brilliant
hunchback with a crown of leaves.

The ailments escaped from the labels
of medicine bottles are all fled to the wind;
I've seen myself lately in the eyes
       of old women,
spent streams mourning my manhood,

in whose old pupils the sun became
a bloodsmear on broad catalpa leaves
and hanging from ancient twigs,
       my murdered selves
sparked the air like the muted collisions
of fruit. A black dog howls down my blood,
a black dog with yellow eyes;
he too by someone's inadvertence
       saw the bloodsmear
on the broad catalpa leaves.

But the furies clear a path for me to the worm
who sang for an hour in the throat of a robin,
and misled by the cries of young boys
       I am again
a breathless swimmer in that cold green element.

I have seen the Bird of Paradise, she has spread herself before me, and I shall never be the same again.

There is nothing to be afraid of. Nothing.

Exactly.

The Life I am trying to grasp is the me that is trying to grasp it.

              R.D. Laing, *The Bird of Paradise*

Flower Arranger
Joy Kogawa

Among the weedy steel structures
And frenetic flowering of factories
I found a blind flower arranger
In a sketch of a room
Dipping a drop of water
Onto an opening petal
Of a tiny not quite flowering bud.
With his fingertips
He placed gentleness in the air
And everywhere among the blowing weeds
He moved with his outstretched hands
Touching the air
With his transient dew.

Perspective
Stuart Mackinnon

Climbing a mountain I am nothing;
I am vaguely seen within the green tree;
and the river turns quicker than my eye.

I can upstage them manfully
and bear them, as you can see
if they become my background,
since only in the human form
can you regard their qualities together.

The eye, slivered by the wave's light
sees faces in the leaves,
and comes upon a distant mountain
with longing for a half-remembered
   body.

"When a warrior has acquired patience he is on his way to will. He knows how to wait. His death sits with him on his mat, they are friends. His death advises him, in mysterious ways, how to choose, how to live strategically. And the warrior waits! I would say that the warrior learns without any hurry because he knows he is waiting for his will; and one day he succeeds in performing something ordinarily quite impossible to accomplish. He may not even notice his extraordinary deed. But as he keeps on performing impossible acts, or as impossible things keep on happening to him, he becomes aware that a sort of power is emerging. A power that comes out of his body as he progresses on the path of knowledge. At first it is like an itching on the belly, or a warm spot that cannot be soothed; then it becomes a pain, a great discomfort. Sometimes the pain and discomfort are so great that the warrior has convulsions for months, the more severe the convulsions the better for him. A fine power is always heralded by great pain.

"When the convulsions cease the warrior notices he has strange feelings about things. He notices that he can actually touch anything he wants with a feeling that comes out of his body from a spot right below or right above his navel. That feeling is the will, and when he is capable of grabbing with it, one can rightfully say that the warrior is a sorcerer, and that he has acquired will."

Carlos Castaneda, *A Separate Reality*

Coming Home on the Ox's Back

The struggle is over; the man is no more concerned with gain and loss. Saddling
himself on the ox's back, his eyes are fixed on things not of the
earth, earthy. Even if he is called, he will not turn his head;
however enticed he will no more be kept back.

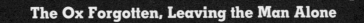

The Ox Forgotten, Leaving the Man Alone

When you know that what you need is not the snare or set-net but the hare or fish,
it is like gold separated from the dross. The one ray of light serene
and penetrating shines even before days of creation. Riding on the animal, he is
at last back in his home, where lo! the ox is no more; the
man alone sits serenely. Though the red sun is high up he is still quietly
dreaming, his whip and rope idly lying.

Fern Hill
Dylan Thomas

Now as I was young and easy under the apple boughs
About the lilting house and happy as the grass was green,
    The night above the dingle starry,
      Time let me hail and climb
    Golden in the heydays of his eyes,
And honoured among wagons I was prince of the apple towns
And once below a time I lordly had the trees and leaves
      Trail with daisies and barley
    Down the rivers of the windfall light.

And as I was green and carefree, famous among the barns
About the happy yard and singing as the farm was home,
    In the sun that is young once only,
      Time let me play and be
    Golden in the mercy of his means,
And green and golden I was huntsman and herdsman, the calves
Sang to my horn, the foxes on the hills barked clear and cold,
      And the sabbath rang slowly
    In the pebbles of the holy streams.

All the sun long it was running, it was lovely, the hay
Fields high as the house, the tunes from the chimneys, it was air
    And playing, lovely and watery
      And fire green as grass.
    And nightly under the simple stars
As I rode to sleep the owls were bearing the farm away,
All the moon long I heard, blessed among stables, the nightjars
    Flying with the ricks, and the horses
      Flashing into the dark.

And then to awake, and the farm, like a wanderer white
With the dew, come back, the cock on his shoulder: it was all
    Shining, it was Adam and maiden,
      The sky gathered again
    And the sun grew round that very day.
So it must have been after the birth of the simple light
In the first, spinning place, the spellbound horses walking warm
    Out of the whinnying green stable
      On to the fields of praise.

And honoured among foxes and pheasants by the gay house
Under the new made clouds and happy as the heart was long,
    In the sun born over and over,
      I ran my heedless ways,
    My wishes raced through the house high hay
And nothing I cared, at my sky blue trades, that time allows
In all his tuneful turning so few and such morning songs
    Before the children green and golden
      Follow him out of grace,

Nothing I cared, in the lamb white days, that time would take me
Up to the swallow thronged loft by the shadow of my hand,
    In the moon that is always rising,
      Nor that riding to sleep
    I should hear him fly with the high fields
And wake to the farm forever fled from the childless land.
Oh as I was young and easy in the mercy of his means,
      Time held me green and dying
    Though I sang in my chains like the sea.

In the wilderness I soon became melancholy. I would sometimes fall to weeping and feel unhappy without knowing why. Then for no reason all would suddenly be changed, and I felt a great, inexplicable joy, a joy so powerful that I could not restrain it, but had to break into song, a mighty song, with room for only one word: joy, joy! And I had to use the full strength of my voice. And then in the midst of such a fit of mysterious and over-whelming delight I became a shaman, not knowing myself how it came about. But I was a shaman. I could see and hear in a totally different way. I had gained my enlightenment, the shaman's light of brain and body, and this in such a manner that it was not only I who could see through the darkness of life, but the same bright light also shone out from me, imperceptible to human beings but visible to all spirits of earth and sky and sea, and these now came to me to become my helping spirit.

Told by an Eskimo shaman to K. Rasmussen,
The Intellectual Culture of the Iglulik Eskimos

Once upon a time, I, Chuang Tzu, dreamt I was a butter-fly, fluttering hither and thither, to all intents and purposes a butterfly. I was conscious only of following my fancies as a butterfly, and was unconscious of my individuality as a man. Suddenly, I awoke, and there I lay, myself again. Now I do not know whether I was then a man dreaming I was a butterfly, or whether I am now a butterfly dreaming I am a man.

Chuang Tzu

Ode
William Wordsworth
**Intimations of Immortality from Recollections
of Early Childhood**

The Child is father of the Man;
And I could wish my days to be
Bound each to each by natural piety.

I

There was a time when meadow, grove, and stream,
The earth, and every common sight,
        To me did seem
        Apparelled in celestial light,
The glory and the freshness of a dream.
It is not now as it hath been of yore;—
        Turn whereso'er I may,
            By night or day,
The things which I have seen I now can see no more.

II

        The Rainbow comes and goes,
        And lovely is the Rose,
        The Moon doth with delight
Look round her when the heavens are bare,
        Waters on a starry night
        Are beautiful and fair;
    The sunshine is a glorious birth;
    But yet I know, where'er I go,
That there hath past away a glory from the earth.

III

Now, while the birds thus sing a joyous song,
        And while the young lambs bound
            As to the tabor's sound,
To me alone there came a thought of grief:
A timely utterance gave that thought relief,
        And I again am strong:
The cataracts blow their trumpets from the steep;
No more shall grief of mine the season wrong;
I hear the Echoes through the mountains throng,
The Winds come to me from the fields of sleep,
        And all the earth is gay;
            Land and sea
        Give themselves up to jollity,
            And with the heart of May
        Doth every Beast keep holiday;—
            Thou Child of Joy,
Shout round me, let me hear thy shouts, thou happy
            Shepherd-boy!

IV

Ye blessèd Creatures, I have heard the call
        Ye to each other make; I see
The heavens laugh with you in your jubilee;
        My heart is at your festival,
        My head hath its coronal,
The fulness of your bliss, I feel—I feel it all.
            Oh evil day! if I were sullen
            While Earth herself is adorning,
                This sweet May-morning,
            And the Children are culling
                On every side,
            In a thousand valleys far and wide,
            Fresh flowers; while the sun shines warm,
And the Babe leaps up on his Mother's arm:—
            I hear, I hear, with joy I hear!
            —But there's a Tree, of many, one,
A single Field which I have looked upon,
Both of them speak of something that is gone:
            The Pansy at my feet
            Doth the same tale repeat:
Whither is fled the visionary gleam?
Where is it now, the glory and the dream?

V

Our birth is but a sleep and a forgetting:
The Soul that rises with us, our life's Star,
        Hath had elsewhere its setting,
            And cometh from afar:
        Not in entire forgetfulness,
        And not in utter nakedness,
But trailing clouds of glory do we come
        From God, who is our home:
Heaven lies about us in our infancy!
Shades of the prison-house begin to close
        Upon the growing Boy,
But He beholds the light, and whence it flows,
        He sees it in his joy;
The Youth, who daily farther from the east
        Must travel, still is Nature's Priest,
            And by the vision splendid
            Is on his way attended;
At length the Man perceives it die away,
And fade into the light of common day.

VI

Earth fills her lap with pleasures of her own;
Yearnings she hath in her own natural kind,
And, even with something of a Mother's mind,
        And no unworthy aim,
        The homely Nurse doth all she can
To make her Foster-child, her Inmate Man,
        Forget the glories he hath known,
And that imperial palace whence he came.

VII

Behold the Child among his new-born blisses,
A six years' Darling of a pigmy size!
See, where 'mid work of his own hand he lies,
Fretted by sallies of his mother's kisses,
With light upon him from his father's eyes!
See, at his feet, some little plan or chart,
Some fragment from his dream of human life,
Shaped by himself with newly-learned art;
        A wedding or a festival,
        A mourning or a funeral;
            And this hath now his heart,
            And unto this he frames his song.
            Then will he fit his tongue
To dialogues of business, love, or strife;

But it will not be long
        Ere this be thrown aside,
        And with new joy and pride
The little Actor cons another part;
Filling from time to time his "humorous stage"
With all the Persons, down to palsied Age,
That Life brings with her in her equipage;
        As if his whole vocation
        Were endless imitation.

VIII

Thou, whose exterior semblance doth belie
        Thy Soul's immensity;
Thou best Philosopher, who yet dost keep
Thy heritage, thou Eye among the blind,
That, deaf and silent, read'st the eternal deep,
Haunted for ever by the eternal mind,—
        Mighty Prophet! Seer blest!
        On whom those truths do rest,
Which we are toiling all our lives to find,
In darkness lost, the darkness of the grave,
Thou, over whom thy Immortality
Broods like the Day, a Master o'er a Slave,
A Presence which is not to be put by;
Thou little Child, yet glorious in the might
Of heaven-born freedom on thy being's height,
Why with such earnest pains dost thou provoke
The years to bring the inevitable yoke,
Thus blindly with thy blessedness at strife?
Full soon thy Soul shall have her earthly freight,
And custom lie upon thee with a weight,
Heavy as frost, and deep almost as life!

IX

        O joy! that in our embers
        Is something that doth live,
        That nature yet remembers
        What was so fugitive!
The thought of our past years in me doth breed
Perpetual benediction: not indeed
For that which is most worthy to be blest;
Delight and liberty, the simple creed
Of Childhood, whether busy or at rest,
With new-fledged hope still fluttering in his breast:—
        Not for these I raise
        The song of thanks and praise;

But for those obstinate questionings
Of sense and outward things,
Fallings from us, vanishings;
Blank misgivings of a Creature
Moving about in worlds not realised,
High instincts before which our mortal Nature
Did tremble like a guilty Thing surprised:
But for those first affections,
Those shadowy recollections,
Which, be they what they may,
Are yet the fountain-light of all our day,
Are yet a master-light of all our seeing;
Uphold us, cherish, and have power to make
Our noisy years seem moments in the being
Of the eternal Silence: truths that wake,
To perish never:
Which neither listlessness, nor mad endeavour,
Nor Man nor Boy,
Nor all that is at enmity with joy,
Can utterly abolish or destroy!
Hence in a season of calm weather
Though inland far we be,
Our Souls have sight of that immortal sea
Which brought us hither,
Can in a moment travel thither,
And see the Children sport upon the shore,
And hear the mighty waters rolling evermore.

X

Then sing, ye Birds, sing, sing a joyous song!
And let the young Lambs bound
As to the tabor's sound!
We in thought will join your throng,
Ye that pipe and ye that play,
Ye that through your hearts today
Feel the gladness of the May!
What though the radiance which was once so bright!
Be now for ever taken from my sight,
Though nothing can bring back the hour
Of splendour in the grass, of glory in the flower;
We will grieve not, rather find
Strength in what remains behind;
In the primal sympathy
Which having been must ever be;
In the soothing thoughts that spring
Out of human suffering;
In the faith that looks through death,
In years that bring the philosophic mind.

XI

And O, ye Fountains, Meadows, Hills, and Groves,
Forebode not any severing of our loves!
Yet in my heart of hearts I feel your might;
I only have relinquished one delight
To live beneath your more habitual sway.
I love the Brooks which down their channels fret,
Even more than when I tripped lightly as they;
The innocent brightness of a new-born Day
Is lovely yet;
The Clouds that gather round the setting sun
Do take a sober colouring from an eye
That hath kept watch o'er man's mortality;
Another race hath been, and other palms are won.
Thanks to the human heart by which we live,
Thanks to its tenderness, its joys, and fears,
To me the meanest flower that blows can give
Thoughts that do often lie too deep for tears.

In an age acid with fear it is still hard for us to see fear as anything but a destructive element, impossible to conceive it as a beginning of wisdom. In a universe like ours contracted to the merely natural, fear means a sour collective terror, a promise of moral collapse and physical annihilation. The Wordsworthian fear, on the other hand, is a solitary emotion, the mood of one for whom being alone is a state both positive and intense. It is also a response to something which, though involved in or symbolised by nature, is felt as superior to nature in the hierarchy of being.

William Walsh, *The Use of Imagination*

Through the imagination some transcendental order which explains the world of appearances and accounts not merely for the existence of visible things but for the affect which they have on us, for the sudden, unpredictable beating of the heart in the presence of beauty, for the conviction that what then moves us cannot be a cheat or an illusion but must derive its authority from the power which moves the Universe.

Harold Bloom, *The Visionary Company*

The Double Vision of Michael Robartes
W.B. Yeats

I

On the grey rock of Cashel the mind's eye
Has called up the cold spirits that are born
When the old moon is vanished from the sky
And the new still hides her horn.

Under blank eyes and fingers never still
The particular is pounded till it is man.
When had I my own will?
O not since life began.

Constrained, arraigned, baffled, bent and unbent
By these wire-jointed jaws and limbs of wood,
Themselves obedient,
Knowing not evil and good;

Obedient to some hidden magical breath.
They do not even feel, so abstract are they,
So dead beyond our death,
Triumph that we obey.

II

On the grey rock of Cashel I suddenly saw
A Sphinx with woman breast and lion paw,
A Buddha, hand at rest,
Hand lifted up that blest;

And right between these two a girl at play
That, it may be, had danced her life away.
For now being dead it seemed
That she of dancing dreamed.

Although I saw it all in the mind's eye
There can be nothing solider till I die;
I saw by the moon's light
Now at its fifteenth night.

One lashed her tail; her eyes lit by the moon
Gazed upon all things known, all things unknown,
In triumph of intellect
With motionless head erect.

That other's moonlit eyeballs never moved,
Being fixed on all things loved, all things unloved.
Yet little peace he had,
For those that love are sad.

O little did they care who danced between,
And little she by whom her dance was seen
So she had outdanced thought.
Body perfection brought,

For what but eye and ear silence the mind
With the minute particulars of mankind?
Mind moved yet seemed to stop
As 'twere a spinning-top.

In contemplation had those three so wrought
Upon a moment, and so stretched it out
That they, time overthrown,
Were dead yet flesh and bone.

III

I knew that I had seen, had seen at last
That girl my unremembering nights hold fast
Or else my dreams that fly
If I should rub an eye,

And yet in flying fling into my meat
A crazy juice that makes the pulses beat
As though I had been undone
By Homer's Paragon

Who never gave the burning town a thought;
To such a pitch of folly I am brought,
Being caught between the pull
Of the dark moon and the full,

The commonness of thought and images
That have the frenzy of our western seas.
Thereon I made my moan,
And after kissed a stone,

And after that arranged it in a song
Seeing that I, ignorant for so long,
Had been rewarded thus
In Cormac's ruined house.

The primary *imagination* I hold to be the living Power
and prime Agent of all human Perception, and as a repetition in the finite mind of the eternal act of creation in
the infinite I *am*.

Samuel Taylor Coleridge

Applelore
Judy Stonehill

Once upon an apple cart
a strange girl threw her lonely limbs.
She swam among the apples there
while singing holy apple hymns.

The maker of the cart turned green
seeing a maiden swimming there.
He leapt into the crimson sea
and tightly pulled her virgin hair.

"Fair Eve, you must climb down at once,
or pay the price of apples sore."
And she replied with tender voice,
"I'm only looking for the core."

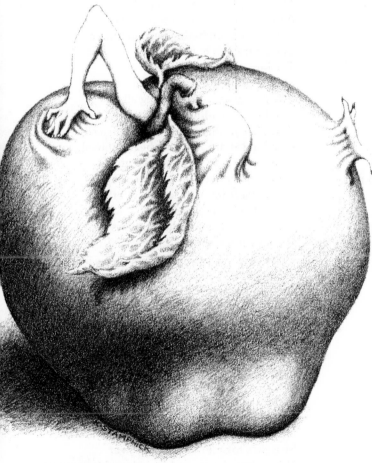

No man shall ever know
    what is true blessedness

Till oneness overwhelm
    and swallow separateness.

Angelus Silesius

Connoisseur of Chaos
Wallace Stevens

I

A.   A violent order is disorder; and
B.   A great disorder is an order. These
Two things are one. (Pages of illustrations.)

II

If all the green of spring was blue, and it is;
If the flowers of South Africa were bright
On the tables of Connecticut, and they are;
If Englishmen lived without tea in Ceylon, and they do;
And if it all went on in an orderly way,
And it does; a law of inherent opposites,
Of essential unity, is as pleasant as port,
As pleasant as the brush-strokes of a bough,
An upper, particular bough in, say, Marchand.

III

After all the pretty contrast of life and death
Proves that these opposite things partake of one,
At least that was the theory, when bishops' books
Resolve the world. We cannot go back to that.
The squirming facts exceed the squamous mind,
If one may say so. And yet relation appears,
A small relation expanding like the shade
Of a cloud on sand, a shape on the side of a hill.

IV

A.   Well, an old order is a violent one.
This proves nothing. Just one more truth, one more
Element in the immense disorder of truths.
B.   It is April as I write. The wind
Is blowing after days of constant rain.
All this, of course, will come to summer soon.
But suppose the disorder of truths should ever come
To an order, most Plantagenet, most fixed . . .
A great disorder as an order. Now, A
And B are not like statuary, posed
For a vista in the Louvre. They are things chalked
On the sidewalk so that the pensive man may see.

V

The pensive man . . . He sees that eagle float
For which the intricate Alps are a single nest.

99

Elijah Browning
Edgar Lee Masters

I was among multitudes of children
Dancing at the foot of a mountain.
A breeze blew out of the east and swept them as leaves,
Driving some up the slopes . . . All was changed.
Here were flying lights, and mystic moons, and dream-music.
A cloud fell upon us. When it lifted all was changed.
I was now amid multitudes who were wrangling.
Then a figure in shimmering gold, and one with a trumpet,
And one with a sceptre stood before me.
They mocked me and danced a rigadoon and vanished. . . .
All was changed again. Out of a bower of poppies
A woman bared her breasts and lifted her open mouth to mine.
I kissed her. The taste of her lips was like salt.
She left blood on my lips. I felt exhausted.
I arose and ascended higher, but a mist as from an iceberg
Clouded my steps. I was cold and in pain.
Then the sun streamed on me again,
And I saw the mists below me hiding all below them.
And I, bent over my staff, knew myself
Silhouetted against the snow. And above me
Was the soundless air, pierced by a cone of ice,
Over which hung a solitary star!
A shudder of ecstacy, a shudder of fear
Ran through me. But I could not return to the slopes—
Nay, I wished not to return.
For the spent waves of the symphony of freedom
Lapped the ethereal cliffs about me.
Therefore I climbed to the pinnacle.
I flung away my staff.
I touched that star
With my outstretched hand.
I vanished utterly.
For the mountain delivers to Infinite Truth
Whosoever touches the star!

The Heavy Bear Who Goes With Me
Delmore Schwartz

The heavy bear who goes with me,
A manifold honey to smear his face,
Clumsy and lumbering here and there,
The central ton of every place,
The hungry beating brutish one
In love with candy, anger, and sleep,
Crazy factotum, dishevelling all,
Climbs the building, kicks the football,
Boxes his brother in the hate-ridden city.
Breathing at my side, that heavy animal,
That heavy bear who sleeps with me,
Howls in his sleep for a world of sugar,
A sweetness intimate as the water's clasp,
Howls in his sleep because the tight-rope
Trembles and shows the darkness beneath.
—The strutting show-off is terrified,
Dressed in his dress-suit, bulging his pants,
Trembles to think that his quivering meat
Must finally wince to nothing at all.

That inescapable animal walks with me,
Has followed me since the black womb held,
Moves where I move, distorting my gesture,
A caricature, a swollen shadow,
A stupid clown of the spirit's motive,
Perplexes and affronts with his own darkness.
The secret life of belly and bone,
Opaque, too near, my private, yet unknown,
Stretches to embrace the very dear
With whom I would walk without him near,
Touches her grossly, although a word
Would bare my heart and make me clear,
Stumbles, flounders, and strives to be fed
Dragging me with him in his mouthing care,
Amid the hundred million of his kind,
The scrimmage of appetite everywhere.

Yoke and Star
José Martí

When I was born, my mother said to me:
"My son, Homagno, Flower of my breast,
Reflected sum of me and of the world,
Fish that to bird and horse and man has turned,
See these two signs of life I offer you
With hope and sorrow. Look and make your choice.
This is a yoke. He who accepts it lives.
By it the ox is tamed, and since he gives
Full service to his master, in warm straw
He sleeps and eats good and abundant oats.
But this, O Mystery sprung from my womb
As peaks from lofty mountain range take shape,
This thing that gleams and slays, this is a star!
All sinners flee from one who bears its mark,
And from its spreading light; and so in life,
As though the one who wears it were a beast
Burdened with crimes, he will be shunned by all.
The man who imitates the care-free ox
Becomes himself a dumb, submissive brute
And has to start again the eternal climb.
But he who, confident, shall choose a star
To be his symbol, grows.
                              When for Mankind
The living person freely pours his cup;
When for the bloody human festival
The good man sacrificed his beating heart
Quickly and gravely; when to wandering winds
Of North and South, he gave his sacred words;
The Star, a mantle now, envelops him
And the clear air is bright, as in festive days,
And the living man, who did not fear to live,
Knows he is not alone in dark and death."

"Give me the yoke, O Mother, so that I
Can stamp it under foot, then let the Star
That lights and kills glow brightly on my brow!"

The Street
Octavio Paz

The street is very long and filled with silence.
I walk in shadow and I trip and fall,
And then get up and walk with unseeing feet
Over the silent stones and the dry leaves,
And someone close behind, tramples them, too.
If I slow down and stop, he also stops.
If I run, so does he. I look. No one!
The whole street seems so dark, with no way out,
And though I turn and turn, I can't escape.
I always find myself on the same street
Where no one waits for me and none pursues.
Where I pursue, a man who trips and falls
Gets up and seeing me, keeps saying: "No one!"

The Circular Ruins

Jorge Luis Borges
Translated by James E. Irby

> And if he left off dreaming about you . . .
> —*Through the Looking Glass*, VI

No one saw him disembark in the unanimous night, no one saw the bamboo canoe sinking into the sacred mud, but within a few days no one was unaware that the silent man came from the South and that his home was one of the infinite villages upstream, on the violent mountainside, where the Zend tongue is not contaminated with Greek and where leprosy is infrequent. The truth is that the obscure man kissed the mud, came up the bank without pushing aside (probably without feeling) the brambles which dilacerated his flesh, and dragged himself, nauseous and bloodstained, to the circular enclosure crowned by a stone tiger or horse, which once was the color of fire and now was that of ashes. This circle was a temple, long ago devoured by fire, which the malarial jungle had profaned and whose god no longer received the homage of men. The stranger stretched out beneath the pedestal. He was awakened by the sun high above. He evidenced without astonishment that his wounds had closed; he shut his pale eyes and slept, not out of bodily weakness but out of determination of will. He knew that this temple was the place required by his invincible purpose; he knew that, downstream, the incessant trees had not managed to choke the ruins of another propitious temple, whose gods were also burned and dead; he knew that his immediate obligation was to sleep. Towards midnight he was awakened by the disconsolate cry of a bird. Prints of bare feet, some figs and a jug told him that men of the region had respectfully spied upon his sleep and were solicitous of his favor or feared his magic. He felt the chill of fear and sought out a burial niche in the dilapidated wall and covered himself with some unknown leaves.

The purpose which guided him was not impossible, though it was supernatural. He wanted to dream a man: he wanted to dream him with minute integrity and insert him into reality. This magical project had exhausted the entire content of his soul; if someone had asked him his own name or any trait of his previous life, he would not have been able to answer. The uninhabited and broken temple suited him, for it was a minimum of visible world; the nearness of the peasants also suited him, for they would see that his frugal necessities were supplied. The rice and fruit of their tribute were sufficient sustenance for his body, consecrated to the sole task of sleeping and dreaming.

At first, his dreams were chaotic; somewhat later, they were of a dialectical nature. The stranger dreamt that he was in the center of a circular amphitheater which in some way was the burned temple: clouds of silent students filled the gradins; the faces of the last ones hung many centuries away and at a cosmic height, but were entirely clear and precise. The man was lecturing to them on anatomy, cosmography, magic; the countenances listened with eagerness and strove to respond with understanding, as if they divined the importance of the examination which would redeem one of them from his state of vain appearance and interpolate him into the world of reality. The man, both in dreams and awake, considered his phantoms' replies, was not deceived by impostors, divined a growing intelligence in certain perplexities. He sought a soul which would merit participation in the universe.

After nine or ten nights, he comprehended with some bitterness that he could expect nothing of those students who passively accepted his doctrines, but that he could of those who, at times, would venture a reasonable contradiction. The former, though worthy of love and affection, could not rise to the state of individuals; the latter pre-existed somewhat more. One afternoon (now his afternoons too were tributaries of sleep, now he remained awake only for a couple of hours at dawn) he dismissed the vast illusory college forever and kept one single student. He was a silent boy, sallow, sometimes obstinate, with sharp features which reproduced those of the dreamer. He was not long disconcerted by his companions' sudden elimination; his progress, after a few special lessons, astounded his teacher. Nevertheless, catastrophe ensued. The man emerged from sleep one day as if from a viscous desert, looked at the vain light of afternoon, which at first he confused with that of dawn, and understood that he had not really dreamt. All that night and all day, the intolerable lucidity of insomnia weighed upon him. He tried to explore the jungle, to exhaust himself; amidst the hemlocks, he was scarcely able to manage a few snatches of feeble sleep, fleetingly mottled with some rudimentary visions which were useless. He tried to convoke the college and had scarcely uttered a few brief words of exhortation, when it became deformed and was extinguished. In his almost perpetual sleeplessness, his old eyes burned with tears of anger.

He comprehended that the effort to mold the incoherent and vertiginous matter dreams are made of was the most arduous task a man could undertake, though he might penetrate all the enigmas of the upper and lower orders: much more arduous than weaving a rope of sand or coining the faceless wind. He comprehended that an initial failure was inevitable. He swore he would forget the enormous hallucination which had misled him at first, and he sought another method. Before putting it into effect, he dedicated a month to replenishing the powers his delirium had wasted. He abandoned any premeditation of dreaming and, almost at once, was able to sleep for a considerable part of the day. The few times he dreamt during this period, he did not take notice of the dreams. To take up his task again, he waited until the moon's disk was perfect. Then, in the afternoon, he purified himself in the waters of the river, worshipped the planetary gods, uttered the lawful syllables of a powerful name and slept. Almost immediately, he dreamt of a beating heart.

He dreamt it as active, warm, secret, the size of a closed fist, of garnet color in the penumbra of a human body as yet without face or sex; with minute love he dreamt it, for fourteen lucid nights. Each night he perceived it with greater clarity. He did not touch it, but limited himself to witnessing it, observing it, perhaps correcting it with his eyes. He perceived it, lived it, from many distances and many angles. On the fourteenth night he touched the pulmonary artery with his finger, and then the whole heart, inside and out. The examination satisfied him. Deliberately, he did not dream for a night; then he took the heart again, invoked the name of a planet and set about to envision another of the principal organs. Within a year he reached the skelton, the eyelids. The innumerable hair was perhaps the most difficult task. He dreamt a complete man, a youth, but this youth could not rise nor did he speak nor could he open his eyes. Night after night, the man dreamt him as asleep.

In the Gnostic cosmogonies, the demiurgi knead and mold a red Adam who cannot stand alone; as unskillful and crude and elementary as this Adam of dust was the Adam of dreams fabricated by the magician's nights of effort. One afternoon, the man almost destroyed his work but then repented. (It would have been better for him had he destroyed it.) Once he had completed his supplications to the numina of the earth and the river, he threw himself down at the feet of the effigy which was perhaps a tiger and perhaps a horse, and implored its unknown succor. That twilight, he dreamt of the statue. He dreamt of it as a living, tremulous thing: it was not an atrocious mongrel of tiger and horse, but both these vehement creatures at once and also a bull, a rose, a tempest. This multiple god revealed to him that its earthly name was Fire, that in the circular temple (and in others of its kind) people had rendered it sacrifices and cult and that it would magically give life to the sleeping phantom, in such a way that all creatures except Fire itself and the dreamer would believe him to be a man of flesh and blood. The man was ordered by the divinity to instruct his creature in its rites, and send him to the other broken temple whose pyramids survived downstream, so that in this deserted edifice a voice might give glory to the god. In the dreamer's dream, the dreamed one awoke.

The magician carried out these orders. He devoted a period of time (which finally comprised two years) to revealing the arcana of the universe and of the fire cult to his dream child. Inwardly, it pained him to be separated from the boy. Under the pretext of pedagogical necessity, each day he prolonged the hours he dedicated to his dreams. He also redid the right shoulder, which was perhaps deficient. At times, he was troubled by the impression that all this had happened before. . . . In general, his days were happy; when he closed his eyes, he would think: *Now I shall be with my son.* Or, less often: *The child I have engendered awaits me and will not exist if I do not go to him.*

Gradually, he accustomed the boy to reality. Once he ordered him to place a banner on a distant peak. The following day, the banner flickered from the mountain top. He tried other analogous experiments, each more daring than the last. He understood with certain bitterness that his son was ready—and perhaps impatient—to be born. That night he kissed him for the first time and sent him to the other temple whose debris showed white downstream, through many leagues of inextricable jungle and swamp. But first (so that he would never know he was a phantom, so that he would be thought a man like others) he instilled into him a complete oblivion of his years of apprenticeship.

The man's victory and peace were dimmed by

weariness. At dawn and at twilight, he would prostrate himself before the stone figure, imagining perhaps that his unreal child was practicing the same rites, in other circular ruins, downstream; at night, he would not dream, or would dream only as all men do. He perceived the sounds and forms of the universe with a certain colorlessness: his absent son was being nurtured with these diminutions of his soul. His life's purpose was complete; the man persisted in a kind of ecstasy. After a time, which some narrators of his story prefer to compute in years and others in lustra, he was awakened one midnight by two boatmen; he could not see their faces, but they told him of a magic man in a temple of the North who could walk upon fire and not be burned. The magician suddenly remembered the words of the god. He recalled that, of all the creatures of the world, fire was the only one that knew his son was a phantom. This recollection, at first soothing, finally tormented him. He feared his son might meditate on his abnormal privilege and discover in some way that his condition was that of a mere image. Not to be a man, to be the projection of another man's dream, what a feeling of humiliation, of vertigo! All fathers are interested in the children

they have procreated (they have permitted to exist) in mere confusion or pleasure; it was natural that the magician should fear for the future of that son, created in thought, limb by limb and feature by feature, in a thousand and one secret nights.

The end of his meditations was sudden, though it was foretold in certain signs. First (after a long drought) a faraway cloud on a hill, light and rapid as a bird; then, toward the south, the sky which had the rose color of the leopard's mouth; then the smoke which corroded the metallic nights; finally, the panicky flight of the animals. For what was happening had happened many centuries ago. The ruins of the fire god's sanctuary were destroyed by fire. In a birdless dawn the magician saw the concentric blaze close round the walls. For a moment, he thought of taking refuge in the river, but then he knew that death was coming to crown his old age and absolve him of his labors. He walked into the shreds of flame. But they did not bite into his flesh, they caressed him and engulfed him without heat or combustion. With relief, with humiliation, with terror, he understood that he too was a mere appearance, dreamt by another.

The universe begins to look more and more like a great thought than a great machine.

Dr. J.B. Rhine

There are two ways of escaping our more or less automatized routines of thinking and behaving. The first, of course, is the plunge into dreaming or dream-like states, when the codes of rational thinking are suspended. The other way is also an escape—from boredom, stagnation, intellectual predicaments, and emotional frustration—but an escape in the opposite direction; it is signalled by the spontaneous flash of insight which shows a familiar situation or event in a new light, and elicits a new response to it. The bisociative act connects previously un-connected matrices of experience; it makes us "understand what it is to be awake, to be living on several planes at once".

Arthur Koestler, *The Act of Creation*

Deep in the nature of every man there is the consciousness of powers which remain latent because there is nothing in his external sphere to give a field to their activity. Deep in the heart of every man, there is the consciousness of a better nature, to the development of which his physical environment is unfavourable. The most sluggish and unspiritual of persons will confess to the possession of aspirations which they would be glad to pursue if it were possible. There is something within them which responds to the great and the noble. There are times when the perfect life seems more eminently beautiful than any of the transient pleasures of a selfish and sensuous existence, however much the tinsel of extrinsic attraction may invest such existence with the ornate adornments of earthly joy. We are aware of the stirring within us of what seems to be a new faculty, a new power, a new purpose, even a new being. In moments of a rare penetration, the outer crust of our ordinary personality appears to dissolve for a little, and the radiance of an inner man transfigures the exterior nature. Something within us is attempting to burst through the hard and material sheath of our actual form of subsistence . . .

Arthur Edward Waite, *Azoth; or, the Star in the East*

Of the Terrible Doubt of Appearances
Walt Whitman

Of the terrible doubt of appearances,
Of the uncertainty after all, that we may be deluded,
That may-be reliance and hope are but speculations after all,
That may-be identity beyond the grave is a beautiful fable only,
May-be the things I perceive, the animals, plants, men, hills,
    shining and flowing waters,
The skies of day and night, colors, densities, forms, may-be these
    are (as doubtless they are) only apparitions, and the real
    something has yet to be known,
(How often they dart out of themselves as if to confound me and
    mock me!
How often I think neither I know, nor any man knows, aught of
    them,)
May-be seeming to me what they are (as doubtless they indeed
    but seem) as from my present point of view, and might
    prove (as of course they would) nought of what they
    appear, or nought anyhow, from entirely changed points
    of view;
To me these and the like of these are curiously answer'd by my
    lovers, my dear friends,
When he whom I love travels with me or sits a long while holding
    me by the hand,
When the subtle air, the impalpable, the sense that words and
    reason hold not, surround us and pervade us,
Then I am charged with untold and untellable wisdom, I am
    silent, I require nothing further,
I cannot answer the question of appearances or that of identity
    beyond the grave,
But I walk or sit indifferent, I am satisfied,
He ahold of my hand has completely satisfied me.

Philosopher in a Landscape
Stuart Mackinnon

Like the children's puzzle
"Can you find the man
in the tree" and you must
turn it in your mind
until the profile is
on solid ground.
           One man
sleeps upside down, his head
over the embankment.
You must turn the tree
upside down to see it
emulate his hair.
Another, say Absalom
is caught by fuzzy branches.
You must turn the world
upside down, if you
wish to see any connection
between ingratitude and trees.

Design
Robert Frost

I found a dimpled spider, fat and white,
On a white heal-all, holding up a moth
Like a white piece of rigid satin cloth—
Assorted characters of death and blight
Mixed ready to begin the morning right,
Like the ingredients of a witches' broth—
A snow-drop spider, a flower like a froth,
And dead wings carried like a paper kite.

What had that flower to do with being white,
The wayside blue and innocent heal-all?
What brought the kindred spider to that height,
Then steered the white moth thither in the night?
What but design of darkness to appall?—
If design govern in a thing so small.

A Recognition
Mark Rudman

There is no end
to being
delivered

midwife
to the self
we play the other

calmly we watch
the dock
sinking

not noticing
who is sitting
on it

and as our nostrils
fill with water
we think

Damn
I should have
known

who else
could it
have been

The Second Coming
W.B. Yeats

Turning and turning in the widening gyre
The falcon cannot hear the falconer;
Things fall apart; the centre cannot hold;
Mere anarchy is loosed upon the world,
The blood-dimmed tide is loosed, and everywhere
The ceremony of innocence is drowned;
The best lack all conviction, while the worst
Are full of passionate intensity.

Surely some revelation is at hand;
Surely the Second Coming is at hand.
The Second Coming! Hardly are those words out
When a vast image out of *Spiritus Mundi*
Troubles my sight: somewhere in sands of the desert
A shape with lion body and the head of a man,
A gaze blank and pitiless as the sun,
Is moving its slow thighs, while all about it
Reel shadows of the indignant desert birds.
The darkness drops again; but now I know
That twenty centuries of stony sleep
Were vexed to nightmare by a rocking cradle,
And what rough beast, its hour come round at last,
Slouches towards Bethlehem to be born?

Nine Lives

Ursula K. Le Guin

She was alive inside, but dead outside, her face a black and dun net of wrinkles, tumors, cracks. She was bald and blind. The tremors that crossed Libra's face were mere quiverings of corruption: underneath, in the black corridors, the halls beneath the skin, there were crepitations in darkness, ferments, chemical nightmares that went on for centuries. "Oh the damned flatulent planet," Pugh murmured as the dome shook and a boil burst a kilometer to the south-west, spraying silver pus across the sunset. The sun had been setting for the last two days. "I'll be glad to see a human face."

"Thanks," said Martin.

"Yours is human to be sure," said Pugh, "but I've seen it so long I can't see it."

Radvid signals cluttered the communicator which Martin was operating, faded, returned as face and voice. The face filled the screen, the nose of an Assyrian king, the eyes of a samurai, skin bronze, eyes the color of iron: young, magnificent. "Is that what human beings look like?" said Pugh with awe. "I'd forgotten."

"Shut up, Owen, we're on."

"Libra Exploratory Mission Base, come in please, this is *Passerine* launch."

"Libra here. Beam fixed. Come on down, launch."

"Expulsion in seven E-seconds. Hold on." The screen blanked and sparkled.

"Do they all look like that? Martin, you and I are uglier men than I thought."

"Shut up, Owen. . . ."

For twenty-two minutes Martin followed the landing-craft down by signal and then through the cleared dome they saw it, small star in the blood-colored east, sinking. It came down neat and quiet, Libra's thin atmosphere carrying little sound. Pugh and Martin closed the headpieces of their imsuits, zipped out of the dome airlocks, and ran with soaring strides, Nijinsky and Nureyev, toward the boat. Three equipment modules came floating down at four-minute intervals from each other and hundred-meter intervals east of the boat. "Come on out," Martin said on his suit radio, "we're waiting at the door."

"Come on in, the methane's fine," said Pugh.

The hatch opened. The young man they had seen on the screen came out with one athletic twist and leaped down onto the shaky dust and clinkers of Libra. Martin shook his hand, but Pugh was staring at the hatch, from which another young man emerged with the same neat twist and jump, followed by a young woman who emerged with the same neat twist, ornamented by a wriggle, and the jump. They were all tall, with bronze skin, black hair, high-bridged noses, epicanthic fold, the same face. They all had the same face. The fourth was emerging from the hatch with a neat twist and jump. "Martin bach," said Pugh, "we've got a clone."

"Right," said one of them, "we're a tenclone. John Chow's the name. You're Lieutenant Martin?"

"I'm Owen Pugh."

"Alvaro Guillen Martin," said Martin, formal, bowing slightly. Another girl was out, the same beautiful face; Martin stared at her and his eye rolled like a nervous pony's. Evidently he had never given any thought to cloning, and was suffering technological shock. "Steady," Pugh said in the Argentine dialect, "it's only excess twins." He stood close by Martin's elbow. He was glad himself of the contact.

It is hard to meet a stranger. Even the greatest extrovert meeting even the meekest stranger knows a certain dread, though he may not know he knows it. Will he make a fool of me wreck my image of myself invade me destroy me change me? Will he be different from me? Yes, that he will. There's the terrible thing: the strangeness of the stranger.

After two years on a dead planet, and the last half year isolated as a team of two, oneself and one other, after that it's even harder to meet a stranger, however welcome he may be. You're out of the habit of difference, you've lost the touch; and so the fear revives, the primitive anxiety, the old dread.

The clone, five males and five females, had got done in a couple of minutes what a man might have got done in twenty: greeted Pugh and Martin, had a glance at Libra, unloaded the boat, made ready to go. They went, and the dome filled with them, a hive of golden bees. They hummed and buzzed quietly, filled up all silences, all spaces with a honey-brown swarm of human presence. Martin looked bewilderedly at the long-limbed girls, and they smiled at him, three at once. Their smile was gentler than that of the boys, but no less radiantly self-possessed.

"Self-possessed," Owen Pugh murmured to his friend, "that's it. Think of it, to be oneself ten times over. Nine seconds for every motion, nine ayes on every vote. It would be glorious!" But Martin was asleep. And the John Chows had all gone to sleep at once. The dome was filled with their quiet breathing. They were young, they didn't snore. Martin sighed and snored, his hershey-bar colored face relaxed in the dim afterglow of Libra's primary, set at last. Pugh had cleared the dome and stars looked in, Sol among them, a great company of lights, a clone of splendors. Pugh slept and dreamed of a one-eyed giant who chased him through the shaking halls of Hell.

From his sleeping-bag Pugh watched the clone's awakening. They all got up within one minute except for one pair, a boy and a girl, who lay snugly tangled and still sleeping in one bag. As Pugh saw this there was a shock like one of Libra's earthquakes inside him, a very deep tremor. He was not aware of this, and in fact thought he was pleased at the sight; there was no other such comfort on this dead hollow world, more power to them, who made love. One of the others stepped on the pair. They woke and the girl sat up flushed and sleepy, with bare golden breasts. One of her sisters murmured something to her; she shot a glance at Pugh and disappeared in the sleeping-bag, followed by a giant giggle, from another direction a fierce stare, from still another direction a voice: "Christ, we're used to having a room to ourselves. Hope you don't mind, Captain Pugh."

"It's a pleasure," Pugh said half-truthfully. He had to stand up then, wearing only the shorts he slept in, and he felt like a plucked rooster, all white scrawn and pimples. He had seldom envied Martin's compact brownness so much. The United Kingdom had come through the Great Famines well, losing less that half its population: a record achieved by rigorous food-control. Black-marketeers and hoarders had been executed. Crumbs had been shared. Where in richer lands most had died and a few had thriven, in Britain fewer died and none throve. They all got lean. Their sons were lean, their grandsons lean, small, brittle-boned, easily infected. When civilization became a matter of standing in lines, the British had kept queue, and so had replaced the survival of the fittest with the survival of the fair-minded. Owen Pugh was a scrawny little man. All the same, he was there.

At the moment he wished he wasn't.

At breakfast a John said, "Now if you'll brief us, Captain Pugh—"

"Owen, then."

"Owen, we can work out our schedule. Anything

new on the mine since your last report to your Mission? We saw your reports when *Passerine* was orbiting Planet V, where they are now."

Martin did not answer, though the mine was his discovery and project, and Pugh had to do his best. It was hard to talk to them. The same faces, each with the same expression of intelligent interest, all leaned toward him across the table at almost the same angle. They all nodded together.

Over the Exploitation Corps insignia on their tunics each had a nameband, first name John and last name Chow of course, but the middle names different. The men were Aleph, Kaph, Yod, Gimel, and Samedh; the women Sadhe, Daleth, Zayin, Beth and Resh. Pugh tried to use the names but gave it up at once; he could not even tell sometimes which one had spoken, for the voices were all alike.

Martin buttered and chewed his toast, and finally interrupted: "You're a team. Is that it?"

"Right," said two Johns.

"God, what a team! I hadn't seen the point. How much do you each know what the others are thinking?"

"Not at all, properly speaking," replied one of the girls, Zayin. The others watched her with the proprietary, approving look they had. "No ESP, nothing fancy. But we think alike. We have exactly the same equipment. Given the same stimulus, the same problem, we're likely to be coming up with the same reactions and solutions at the same time. Explanations are easy—don't even have to make them, usually. We seldom misunderstand each other. It does facilitate our working as a team."

"Christ yes," said Martin. "Pugh and I have spent seven hours out of ten for six months misunderstanding each other. Like most people. What about emergencies, are you as good at meeting the unexpected problem as a nor . . . an unrelated team?"

"Statistics so far indicate that we are," Zayin answered readily. Clones must be trained, Pugh thought, to meet questions, to reassure and reason. All they said had the slightly bland and stilted quality of answers furnished to the Public. "We can't brainstorm as singletons can, we as a team don't profit from the interplay of varied minds; but we have a compensatory advantage. Clones are drawn from the best human material, individuals of IIQ 99th percentile, Genetic Constitution alpha double A, and so on. We have more to draw on than most individuals do."

"And it's multiplied by a factor of ten. Who is—who was John Chow?"

"A genius surely," Pugh said politely. His interest in cloning was not so new and avid as Martin's.

"Leonardo Complex type," said Yod. "Biomath, also a cellist, and an undersea hunter, and interested in structural engineering problems, and so on. Died before he'd worked out his major theories."

"Then you each represent a different facet of his mind, his talents?"

"No, said Zayin, shaking her head in time with several others. "We share the basic equipment and tendencies, of course, but we're all engineers in Planetary Exploitation. A later clone can be trained to develop other aspects of the basic equipment. It's all training; the genetic substance is identical. We *are* John Chow. But we were differently trained."

Martin looked shell-shocked. "How old are you?"

"Twenty-three."

"You say he died young— Had they taken germ cells from him beforehand or something?"

Gimel took over: "He died at twenty-four in an aircar crash. They couldn't save the brain, so they took some intestinal cells and cultured them for cloning. Reproductive cells aren't used for cloning since they have only half the chromosomes. Intestinal cells happen to be easy to despecialize and reprogram for total growth."

"All chips off the old block," Martin said valiantly. "But how can . . . some of you be women . . . ?"

Beth took over: "It's easy to program half the clonal mass back to the female. Just delete the male gene from half the cells and they revert to the basic, that is, the female. It's trickier to go the other way, have to hook in artificial Y chromosomes. So they mostly clone from males, since clones function best bisexually."

Gimel again: "They've worked these matters of technique and function out carefully. The taxpayer wants the best for his money, and of course clones are expensive. With the cell-manipulations, and the incubation in Ngama Placentae, and the maintenance and training of the foster-parent groups, we end up costing about three million apiece."

"For your next generation," Martin said, still struggling, "I suppose you . . . you breed?"

"We females are sterile," said Beth with perfect equanimity; "you remember that the Y chromosome was deleted from our original cell. The males can interbreed with approved singletons, if they want to. But to get John Chow again as often as they want, they just reclone a cell from this clone."

Martin gave up the struggle. He nodded and chewed cold toast. "Well," said one of the Johns, and all changed mood, like a flock of starlings that change course in one wingflick, following a leader so fast that no eye can see which leads. They were ready to go. "How about a look at the mine? Then we'll unload the equipment. Some nice new models in the roboats; you'll want to see them. Right?" Had Pugh or Martin not agreed they might have found it hard to say so. The Johns were polite but unanimous; their decisions carried. Pugh, Commander of Libra Base 2, felt a qualm. Could he boss around this superman-woman-entity-of-ten? and a genius at that? He stuck close to Martin as they suited for outside. Neither said anything.

Four apiece in the three large jetsleds, they slipped off north from the dome, over Libra's dun rugose skin, in starlight.

"Desolate," one said.

It was a boy and girl with Pugh and Martin. Pugh wondered if these were the two that had shared a sleeping-bag last night. No doubt they wouldn't mind if he asked them. Sex must be as handy as breathing, to them. Did you two breathe last night?

"Yes," he said, "it is desolate."

"This is our first time Off, except training on Luna." The girl's voice was definitely a bit higher and softer.

"How did you take the big hop?"

"They doped us. I wanted to experience it." That was the boy; he sounded wistful. They seemed to have more personality, only two at a time. Did repetition of the individual negate individuality?

"Don't worry," said Martin, steering the sled, "you can't experience no-time because it isn't there."

"I'd just like to once," one of them said. "So we'd know."

The Mountains of Merioneth showed leprotic in starlight to the east, a plume of freezing gas trailed silvery from a vent-hole to the west, and the sled tilted groundward. The twins braced for the stop at one moment, each with a slight protective gesture to the other. Your skin is my skin, Pugh thought, but literally, no metaphor. What would it be like, then, to have someone as close to you as that? Always to be answered when you spoke, never to be in pain alone. Love your neighbor as you love yourself. . . . That hard old problem was solved. The neighbor was the self: the love was perfect.

And here was Hellmouth, the mine.

Pugh was the Exploratory Mission's ET geologist, and Martin his technician and cartographer; but when in the course of a local survey Martin had discovered the U-mine, Pugh had given him full credit, as well as the onus of prospecting the lode and planning the Exploitation Team's job. These kids had been sent out from Earth years before Martin's reports got there, and had not known what their job would be until they got here. The Exploitation Corps simply sent out teams regularly and blindly as a dandelion sends out its seeds, knowing there would be a job for them on Libra or the next planet out or one they hadn't even heard about yet. The Government wanted uranium too urgently to wait while reports drifted home across the light-years. The stuff was like gold, old-fashioned but essential, worth mining extraterrestrially and shipping interstellar. Worth its weight in people, Pugh thought sourly, watching the tall young men and women go one by one, glimmering in starlight, into the black hole Martin had named Hellmouth.

As they went in their homeostatic forehead-lamps brightened. Twelve nodding gleams ran along the moist, wrinkled walls. Pugh heard Martin's radiation counter peeping twenty to the dozen up ahead. "Here's the drop-off," said Martin's voice in the suit intercom, drowning out the peeping and the dead silence that was around them. "We're in a side-fissure; this is the main vertical vent in front of us." The black void gaped, its far side not visible in the headlamp beams. "Last vulcanism seems to have been a couple of thousand years ago. Nearest fault is twenty-eight kilos east, in the Trench. This region seems to be as safe seismically as anything in the area. The big basalt-flow overhead stabilizes all these substructures, so long as it remains stable itself. Your central lode is thirty-six meters down and runs in a series of five bubble-caverns northeast. It is a lode, a pipe of very high-grade ore. You saw the percentage figures, right? Extraction's going to be no problem. All you've got to do is get the bubbles topside."

"Take off the lid and let 'em float up." A chuckle. Voices began to talk, but they were all the same voice and the suit radio gave them no location in space. "Open the thing right up. —Safer that way. —But it's a solid basalt roof, how thick, ten meters here? —Three to twenty, the report said. —Blow good ore all over the lot. —Use this access we're in, straighten it a bit and run slider-rails for the robos. —Import burros. —Have we got enough propping material? —What's your estimate of total payload mass, Martin?"

"Say over five million kilos and under eight."

"Transport will be here in ten E-months. —It'll have to go pure. —No, they'll have the mass problem in NAFAL shipping licked by now; remember it's been sixteen years since we left Earth last Tuesday. —Right, they'll send the whole lot back and purify it in Earth orbit. —Shall we go down, Martin?"

"Go on. I've been down."

The first one—Aleph? (Heb., the ox, the leader) —swung onto the ladder and down; the rest followed. Pugh and Martin stood at the chasm's edge. Pugh set his intercom to exchange only with Martin's suit, and noticed Martin doing the same. It was a bit wearing, this listening to one person think aloud in ten voices, or was it one voice speaking the thoughts of ten minds?

"A great gut," Pugh said, looking down into the black pit, its veined and warted walls catching stray gleams of head-lamps far below. "A cow's bowel. A bloody great constipated intestine."

Martin's counter peeped like a lost chicken. They stood inside the epileptic planet, breathing oxygen from tanks, wearing suits impermeable to corrosives and harmful radiations, resistant to a two-hundred-degree range of temperatures, tear-proof, and as shock-resistant as possible given the soft vulnerable stuff inside.

"Next hop," Martin said, "I'd like to find a planet that has nothing whatever to exploit."

"You found this."

"Keep me home next time."

Pugh was pleased. He had hoped Martin would want to go on working with him, but neither of them was used to talking much about their feelings, and he had hesitated to ask. "I'll try that," he said.

"I hate this place. I like caves, you know. It's why I came in here. Just spelunking. But this one's a bitch. Mean. You can't ever let down in here. I guess this lot can handle it, though. They know their stuff."

"Wave of the future, whatever," said Pugh.

The wave of the future came swarming up the ladder, swept Martin to the entrance, gabbled at and around him: "Have we got enough material for supports? —If we convert one of the extractor-servos to anneal, yes. —Sufficient if we miniblast? —Kaph can calculate stress."

Pugh had switched his intercom back to receive them; he looked at them, so many thoughts jabbering in an eager mind, and at Martin standing silent among them, and at Hellmouth, and the wrinkled plain. "Settled! How does that strike you as a preliminary schedule, Martin?"

"It's your baby," Martin said.

Within five E-days the Johns had all their material and equipment unloaded and operating, and were starting to open up the mine. They worked with total efficiency. Pugh was fascinated and frightened by their effectiveness, their confidence, their independence. He was no use to them at all. A clone, he thought, might indeed be the first truly stable, self-relient human being. Once adult it would need nobody's help. It would be sufficient to itself physically, sexually, emotionally, intellectually. Whatever he did, any member of it would always receive the support and approval of his peers, his other selves. Nobody else was needed.

Two of the clone stayed in the dome doing calculations and paperwork, with frequent sled-trips to the mine for measurements and tests. They were the mathematicians of the clone, Zayin and Kaph. That is, as Zayin explained, all ten had had thorough mathematical training from age three to twenty-one, but from twenty-one to twenty-three she and Kaph had gone on with math while the others intensified other specialties, geology, mining engineering, electronic engineering, equipment robotics, applied atomics, and so on. "Kaph and I feel," she said, "that we're the element of the clone closest to what John Chow was in his singleton lifetime. But of course he was principally in biomath, and they didn't take us far in that."

"They needed us most in this field," Kaph said, with the patriotic priggishness they sometimes evinced.

Pugh and Martin soon could distinguish this pair from the others, Zayin by gestalt, Kaph only by a discolored left fourth fingernail, got from an ill-aimed hammer at the age of six. No doubt there were many such differences, physical and psychological, among them; nature might be identical, nurture could not be. But the differences were hard to find. And part of the difficulty was that they really never talked to Pugh and Martin. They joked with them, were polite, got along fine. They gave nothing. It was nothing one could complain about; they were very pleasant, they had the standardized American friendliness. "Do you come from Ireland, Owen?"

"Nobody comes from Ireland, Zayin."

"There are lots of Irish-Americans."

"To be sure, but no more Irish. A couple of thousand in all the island, the last I knew. They didn't go in for birth-control, you know, so the food ran out. By the Third Famine there were no Irish left at all but the priesthood, and they were all celibate, or nearly all."

Zayin and Kaph smiled stiffly. They had no experience of either bigotry or irony. "What are you then, ethnically?" Kaph asked, and Pugh replied, "A Welshman."

"Is it Welsh that you and Martin speak together?"

None of your business, Pugh thought, but said, "No, it's his dialect, not mine: Argentinean. A descendant of Spanish."

"You learned it for private communication?"

"Whom had we here to be private from? It's just that sometimes a man likes to speak his native language."

"Ours is English," Kaph said unsympathetically. Why should they have sympathy? That's one of the things you give because you need it back.

"Is Wells quaint?" asked Zayin.

"Wells? Oh, Wales, it's called. Yes. Wales is quaint." Pugh switched on his rock-cutter, which prevented further conversation by a synapse-destroying whine, and while it whined he turned his back and said a profane word in Welsh.

That night he used the Argentine dialect for private communication. "Do they pair off in the same couples, or change every night?"

Martin looked surprised. A prudish expression, unsuited to his features, appeared for a moment. It faded. He too was curious. "I think it's random."

"Don't whisper, man, it sounds dirty. I think they rotate."

"On a schedule?"

"So nobody gets omitted."

Martin gave a vulgar laugh and smothered it. "What about us? Aren't we omitted."

"That doesn't occur to them."

"What if I proposition one of the girls?"

"She'd tell the others and they'd decide as a group."

"I am not a bull," Martin said, his dark, heavy face heating up. "I will not be judged—"

"Down, down, *machismo*," said Pugh. "Do you mean to proposition one?"

Martin shrugged sullen. "Let 'em have their incest."

"Incest is it, or masturbation?"

"I don't care, if they'd do it out of earshot!"

The clone's early attempts at modesty had soon worn off, unmotivated by any deep defensiveness of self or awareness of others. Pugh and Martin were daily deeper swamped under the intimacies of its constant emotional-sexual-mental interchange: swamped yet excluded.

"Two months to go," Martin said one evening.

"To what?" snapped Pugh. He was edgy lately and Martin's sullenness got on his nerves.

"To relief."

In sixty days the full crew of their Exploratory Mission were due back from their survey of the other planets of the system. Pugh was aware of this.

"Crossing off the days on your calendar?" he jeered.

"Pull yourself together, Owen."

"What do you mean?"

"What I say."

They parted in contempt and resentment.

Pugh came in after a day alone on the Pampas, a vast lava-plain the nearest edge of which was two hours south by jet. He was tired, but refreshed by solitude. They were not supposed to take long trips alone, but lately had often done so. Martin stooped under bright lights, drawing one of his elegant, masterly charts: this one was of the whole face of Libra, the cancerous face. The dome was otherwise empty, seeming dim and large as it had before the clone came. "Where's the golden horde?"

Martin grunted ignorance, crosshatching. He straightened his back to glance around at the sun, which squatted feebly like a great red toad on the eastern plain, and at the clock, which said 18:45. "Some big quakes today," he said, returning to his map. "Feel them down there? Lot of crates were falling around. Take a look at the seismo."

The needle jigged and wavered on the roll. It never stopped dancing here. The roll had recorded five quakes of major intensity back in mid-afternoon; twice the needle had hopped off the roll. The attached computer had been activated to emit a slip reading, "Epicenter 61' N by 4'24" E."

"Not in the Trench this time."

"I thought it felt a bit different from usual. Sharper."

"In Base One I used to lie awake all night feeling the ground jump. Queer how you get used to things."

"Go spla if you didn't. What's for dinner?"

"I thought you'd have cooked it."

"Waiting for the clone."

Feeling put upon, Pugh got out a dozen dinner-boxes, stuck two in the Instobake, pulled them out. "All right, here's dinner."

"Been thinking," Martin said, coming to the table. "What if some clone cloned itself? Illegally. Made a thousand duplicates—ten thousand. Whole army. They could make a tidy power-grab, couldn't they?"

"But how many millions did this lot cost to rear? Artificial placentae and all that. It would be hard to keep secret, unless they had a planet to themselves. . . . Back before the Famines when Earth had national governments, they talked about that: clone your best soldiers, have whole regiments of them. But the food ran out before they could play that game."

They talked amicably, as they used to do.

"Funny," Martin said, chewing. "They left early this morning, didn't they?"

"All but Kaph and Zayin. They thought they'd get the first payload aboveground today. What's up?"

"They weren't back for lunch."

"They won't starve to be sure."

"They left at seven."

"So they did." Then Pugh saw it. The air-tanks held eight hours supply.

"Kaph and Zayin carried out spare cans when they left. Or they've got a heap out there."

"They did, but they brought the whole lot in to recharge." Martin stood up, pointing to one of the stacks of stuff that cut the dome into rooms and alleys.

"There's an alarm signal on every imsuit."

"It's not automatic."

Pugh was tired and still hungry. "Sit down and eat, man. That lot can look after themselves."

Martin sat down, but did not eat. "There was a big quake, Owen. The first one. Big enough, it scared me."

After a pause Pugh sighed and said, "All right."

Unenthusiastically, they got out the two-man sled that was always left for them, and headed it north. The long sunrise covered everything in poisonous red jello. The horizontal light and shadow made it hard to see, raised walls of fake iron ahead of them through which they slid, turned the convex plain beyond Hellmouth into a great dimple full of bloody water. Around the tunnel entrance a wilderness of machinery stood, cranes and cables and servos and wheels and diggers and robocarts and sliders and control-huts, all slanting and bulking incoherently in the red light. Martin jumped from the sled, ran into the mine. He came out again, to Pugh. "Oh God, Owen, it's down," he said. Pugh went in and saw, five meters from the entrance, the shiny, moist, black wall that ended the tunnel. Newly exposed to air, it looked organic, like visceral tissue. The tunnel entrance, enlarged by blasting and double-tracked for robocarts, seemed unchanged until he noticed thousands of tiny spiderweb cracks in the walls. The floor was wet with some sluggish fluid.

"They were inside," Martin said.

"They may be still. They surely had extra air-cans—"

"Look, Owen, look at the basalt flow, at the roof; don't you see what the quake did, look at it."

The low hump of land that roofed the caves still had the unreal look of an optical illusion. It had reversed itself, sunk down, leaving a vast dimple or pit. When Pugh walked on it he saw that it too was cracked with many tiny fissures. From some a whitish gas was seeping, so that the sunlight on the surface of the gas-pool was shafted as if by the waters of a dim red lake.

"The mine's not on the fault. There's no fault here!"

Pugh came back to him quickly. "No, there's no fault, Martin. Look, they surely weren't all inside together."

Martin followed him and searched among the wrecked machines dully, then actively. He spotted the airsled. It had come down heading south, and stuck at an angle in a pothole of colloidal dust. It had carried two riders. One was half sunk in the dust, but his suit-meters registered normal functioning; the other hung strapped onto the tilted sled. Her imsuit had burst open on the broken legs, and the body was frozen hard as any rock. That was all they found. As both regulation and custom demanded, they cremated the dead at once with the laser-guns they carried by regulation and had never used before. Pugh, knowing he was going to be sick, wrestled the survivor onto the two-man sled and sent Martin off to the dome with him. Then he vomited, and flushed the waste out of his suit, and finding one four-man sled undamaged followed after Martin, shaking as if the cold of Libra had got through to him.

The survivor was Kaph. He was in deep shock. They found a swelling on the occiput that might mean concussion, but no fracture was visible.

Pugh brought two glasses of food-concentrate and two chasers of aquavit. "Come on," he said. Martin obeyed, drinking off the tonic. They sat down on crates near the cot and sipped the aquavit.

Kaph lay immobile, face like beeswax, hair bright black to the shoulders, lips stiffly parted for faintly gasping breaths.

"It must have been the first shock, the big one," Martin said. "It must have slid the whole structure sideways. Till it fell in on itself. There must be gas layers in the lateral rocks, like those formations in the Thirty-first Quadrant. But there wasn't any sign—" As he spoke the world slid out from under them. Things leaped and clattered, hopped and jigged, shouted Ha! Ha! Ha! "It was like this at fourteen hours," said Reason shakily in Martin's voice; amidst the unfastening and ruin of the world. But Unreason sat up, as the tumult lessened and things ceased dancing, and screamed aloud.

Pugh leaped across his spilled aquavit and held Kaph down. The muscular body flailed him off. Martin pinned the shoulders down. Kaph screamed, struggled, choked; his face blackened. "Oxy," Pugh said, and his hand found the right needle in the medical kit as if by homing instinct; while Martin held the mask he struck the needle home to the vagus nerve, restoring Kaph to life.

"Didn't know you knew that stunt," Martin said, breathing hard.

"The Lazarus Jab; my father was a doctor. It doesn't often work," Pugh said. "I want that drink I spilled. Is the quake over? I can't tell."

"Aftershocks. It's not just you shivering."

"Why did he suffocate?"

"I don't know, Owen. Look in the book."

Kaph was breathing normally and his color was restored, only the lips were still darkened. They poured a new shot of courage and sat down by him again with their medical guide. "Nothing about cyanosis or asphyxiation under 'shock' or 'concussion.' He can't have breathed in anything with his suit on. I don't know. We'd get as much good out of *Mother Mog's Home Herbalist*. . . . 'Anal Hemorrhoids,' fy!" Pugh pitched the book to a crate-table. It fell short, because either Pugh or the table was still unsteady.

"Why didn't he signal?"

"Sorry?"

"The eight inside the mine never had time. But he

and the girl must have been outside. Maybe she was in the entrance, and got hit by the first slide. He must have been outside, in the control-hut maybe. He ran in, pulled her out, strapped her onto the sled, started for the dome. And all that time never pushed the panic button in his imsuit. Why not?"

"Well, he'd had that whack on his head. I doubt he ever realized the girl was dead. He wasn't in his senses. But if he had been I don't know if he'd have thought to signal us. They looked to one another for help."

Martin's face was like an Indian mask, grooves at the mouth-corners, eyes of dull coal. "That's so. What must he have felt, then, when the quake came and he was outside, alone—"

In answer Kaph screamed.

He came up off the cot in the heaving convulsions of one suffocating, knocked Pugh right down with his flailing arm, staggered into a stack of crates and fell to the floor, lips blue, eyes white. Martin dragged him

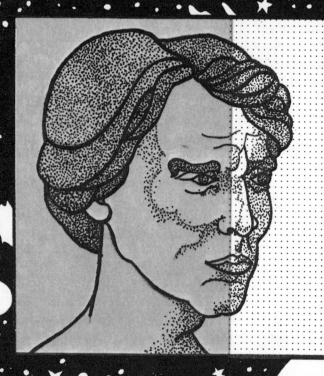

back onto the cot and gave him a whiff of oxygen, then knelt by Pugh, who was just sitting up, and wiped at his cut cheekbone. "Owen, are you all right, are you going to be all right, Owen?"

"I think I am," Pugh said. "Why are you rubbing that on my face?"

It was a short length of computer-tape, now spotted with Pugh's blood. Martin dropped it. "Thought it was a towel. You clipped your cheek on that box there."

"Is he out of it?"

"Seems to be."

They stared down at Kaph lying stiff, his teeth a white line inside dark parted lips.

"Like epilepsy. Brain damage maybe?"

"What about shooting him full of meprobamate?"

Pugh shook his head. "I don't know what's in that shot I already gave him for shock. Don't want to overdose him."

"Maybe he'll sleep it off now."

"I'd like to myself. Between him and the earthquake I can't seem to keep on my feet."

"You got a nasty crack there. Go on, I'll sit up a while."

Pugh cleaned his cut cheek and pulled off his shirt, then paused.

"Is there anything we ought to have done—have tried to do—"

"They're all dead," Martin said heavily, gently.

Pugh lay down on top of his sleeping-bag, and one instant later was awakened by a hideous, sucking, struggling noise. He staggered up, found the needle, tried three times to jab it in correctly and failed, began to massage over Kaph's heart. "Mouth-to-mouth," he said, and Martin obeyed. Presently Kaph drew a harsh breath, his heartbeat steadied, his rigid muscles began to relax.

"How long did I sleep?"

"Half an hour."

They stood up sweating. The ground shuddered, the fabric of the dome sagged and swayed. Libra was dancing her awful polka again, her Totentanz. The sun, though rising, seemed to have grown larger and redder; gas and dust must have been stirred up in the feeble atmosphere.

"What's wrong with him, Owen?"

"I think he's dying with them."

"Them—But they're dead, I tell you."

"Nine of them. They're all dead, they were crushed or suffocated. They were all him, he is all of them. They died, and now he's dying their deaths one by one."

"Oh pity of God," said Martin.

The next time was much the same. The fifth time was worse, for Kaph fought and raved, trying to speak but getting no words out, as if his mouth were stopped with rocks or clay. After that the attacks grew weaker, but so did he. The eighth seizure came at about four-thirty; Pugh and Martin worked till five-thirty doing all they could to keep life in the body that slid without protest into death. They kept him, but Martin said, "The next will finish him." And it did; but Pugh breathed his own breath into the inert lungs, until he himself passed out.

He woke. The dome was opaqued and no light on. He listened and heard the breathing of two sleeping men. He slept, and nothing woke him till hunger did.

The sun was well up over the dark plains, and the planet had stopped dancing. Kaph lay asleep. Pugh and Martin drank tea and looked at him with proprietary triumph.

When he woke Martin went to him: "How do you feel, old man?" There was no answer. Pugh took Martin's place and looked into the brown, dull eyes that gazed toward but not into his own. Like Martin he quickly turned away. He heated food-concentrate and brought it to Kaph. "Come on, drink."

He could see the muscles in Kaph's throat tighten. "Let me die," the young man said.

"You're not dying."

Kaph spoke with clarity and precision: "I am nine-tenths dead. There is not enough of me left alive."

That precision convinced Pugh, and he fought the conviction. "No," he said, peremptory. "They are dead. The others. Your brothers and sisters. You're not them, you're alive. You are John Chow. Your life is in your own hands."

The young man lay still, looking into a darkness that was not there.

Martin and Pugh took turns taking the Exploitation hauler and a spare set of robos over to Hellmouth to salvage equipment and protect it from Libra's sinister atmosphere, for the value of the stuff was, literally, astronomical. It was slow work for one man at a time, but they were unwilling to leave Kaph by himself. The one left in the dome did paperwork, while Kaph sat or lay and stared into his darkness, and never spoke. The days went by silent.

The radio spat and spoke: the Mission calling from ship. "We'll be down on Libra in five weeks, Owen. Thirty-four E-days nine hours I make it as of now. How's tricks in the old dome?"

"Not good, chief. The Exploit team were killed, all but one of them, in the mine. Earthquake. Six days ago."

The radio crackled and sang starsong. Sixteen seconds lag each way; the ship was out around Planet II now. "Killed, all but one? You and Martin were unhurt?"

"We're all right, chief."

Thirty-two seconds.

"*Passerine* left an Exploit team out here with us. I may put them on the Hellmouth project then, instead of the Quadrant Seven project. We'll settle that when we come down. In any case you and Martin will be relieved at Dome Two. Hold tight. Anything else?"

"Nothing else."

Thirty-two seconds.

"Right then. So long, Owen."

Kaph had heard all this, and later on Pugh said to him, "The chief may ask you to stay here with the other Exploit team. You know the ropes here." Knowing the exigencies of Far Out Life, he wanted to warn the young man. Kaph made no answer. Since he had said, "There is not enough of me left alive," he had not spoken a word.

"Owen," Martin said on suit intercom, "he's spla. Insane. Psycho."

"He's doing very well for a man who's died nine times."

"Well? Like a turned-off android is well? The only emotion he has left is hate. Look at his eyes."

"That's not hate, Martin. Listen, it's true that he has, in a sense, been dead. I cannot imagine what he feels. But it's not hatred. He can't even see us. It's too dark."

"Throats have been cut in the dark. He hates us because we're not Aleph and Yod and Zayin."

"Maybe. But I think he's alone. He doesn't see us or hear us, that's the truth. He never had to see anyone else before. He never was alone before. He had himself to see, talk with, live with, nine other selves all his life. He doesn't know how you go it alone. He must learn. Give him time."

Martin shook his heavy head. "Spla," he said. "Just remember when you're alone with him that he could break your neck one-handed."

"He could do that," said Pugh, a short, soft-voiced man with a scarred cheekbone; he smiled. They were just outside the dome airlock, programming one of the servos to repair a damaged hauler. They could see Kaph sitting inside the great half-egg of the dome like a fly in amber.

"Hand me the insert pack there. What makes you think he'll get any better?"

"He has a strong personality, to be sure."

"Strong? Crippled. Nine-tenths dead, as he put it."

"But he's not dead. He's a live man: John Kaph Chow. He had a jolly queer upbringing, but after all every boy has got to break free of his family. He will do it."

"I can't see it."

"Think a bit, Martin bach. What's this cloning for? To repair the human race. We're in a bad way. Look at me. My IIQ and GC are half this John Chow's. Yet they wanted me so badly for the Far Out Service that when I volunteered they took me and fitted me out with an artificial lung and corrected my myopia. Now if there were enough good sound lads about would they be taking one-lunged shortsighted Welshmen?"

"Didn't know you had an artificial lung."

"I do then. Not tin, you know. Human, grown in a tank from a bit of somebody; cloned, if you like. That's how they make replacement-organs, the same general idea as cloning, but bits and pieces instead of whole people. It's my own lung now, whatever. But what I am saying is this, there are too many like me these days, and not enough like John Chow. They're trying to raise the level of the human genetic pool, which is a mucky little puddle since the population crash. So then if a man is cloned, he's a strong and clever man. It's only logic, to be sure."

Martin grunted; the servo began to hum.

Kaph had been eating little; he had trouble swallowing his food, choking on it, so that he would give up trying after a few bites. He had lost eight or ten kilos. After three weeks or so, however, his appetite began to pick up, and one day he began to look through the clone's possessions, the sleeping-

---

By whatever name, there is an impending sense of change in the world of ideas. The reigning wisdom that informed and compelled the past few decades is under attack—or, at the very least, under cross-examination. That wisdom has been variously called liberalism, rationalism, scientism: concepts certainly not identical but related. But now man's confidence in his power to control his world is at a low ebb. Technology is seen as a dangerous ally, and progress is suspect. Even the evolutionists share this unease; their hope lies not in man as he is but in some mutant superman.

Time, April 23, 1973

---

bags, kits, papers which Pugh had stacked neatly in a far angle of a packing-crate alley. He sorted, destroyed a heap of papers and oddments, made a small packet of what remained, then relapsed into his walking coma.

Two days later he spoke. Pugh was trying to correct a flutter in the tape-player, and failing; Martin had the jet out, checking their maps of the Pampas. "Hell and damnation!" Pugh said, and Kaph said in a toneless voice, "Do you want me to do that?"

Pugh jumped, controlled himself, and gave the machine to Kaph. The young man took it apart, put it back together, and left it on the table.

"Put on a tape," Pugh said with careful casualness, busy at another table.

Kaph put on the topmost tape, a chorale. He lay down on his cot. The sound of a hundred human voices singing together filled the dome. He lay still, his face blank.

In the next days he took over several routine jobs,

"Good night," Martin said; Kaph did not.

Next morning at breakfast Kaph reached across Martin's plate for the toast. "Why don't you ask for it," Martin said with the geniality of repressed exasperation. "I can pass it."

"I can reach it," Kaph said in his flat voice.

"Yes, but look. Asking to pass things, saying good night or hello, they're not important, but all the same

---

Professor S. Zamenhof and his team at the University of California have tried injecting pregnant mice and rats with pituitary growth hormone, while the brain of the offspring was still maturing. They gave injections from the seventh to the twelfth day of pregnancy. Subsequently they killed the offspring and examined their brains closely. They found not only a significant increase in brain weight but also an increase in the ratio of neurones to the supporting glial cells. More important still, they discovered that the density of cells in the cortex, where reasoning is carried out, was increased and that the number and length of the dendrites–the branching interconnections–was greater. . . .

At the university of Witwatersrand, the Dean of the Medical Faculty, Professor O.S. Heyns, developed a technique of keeping pregnant women with their abdomen and pelvis inside a plastic enclosure, the pressure in which is reduced by a pump to one-fifth atmospheric pressure, a procedure he calls decompression, or foetal oxygenation. The treatment is given for half an hour daily, during the last ten days of pregnancy and during the beginning of labour. The reduction in pressure on the uterus was planned to reduce the pains of childbirth, and it also helps the maternal blood to circulate more freely.

Professor Heyns was surprised when, a year or so after his first experiments, he began to get reports from their mothers that the children born in these conditions were exceptionally intelligent, and certainly forward in their

physical development. At first these reports were ignored on the grounds that all mothers believe their new baby to be exceptional. But soon it was found that some of these super-oxygenated babies really were exceptional–like Katl Oertel, who was answering the telephone at 13 months, and was speaking in four languages by the age of three. (these babies commonly hear four languages spoken around them–English, German, Zulu, and Afrikaans–but normal babies speak the tongue their mother speaks to them.) These super-children were bored at their nursery schools; they chat with adults in a fluent, unconcerned sort of way which suggests a maturity which usually comes far later. A vocabulary of 200 words by age 18 months is common with them: the average child speaks only half a dozen words at this age.

In the last weeks of pregnancy, the placenta does not grow any further, and the infant's heart becomes incapable of driving blood through it. Professor Heyns believes that, in consequence, the brains of most foetuses fail to develop to their full capacity since the foetus's oxygen demands outstrip the capacity of the mother to supply it. The oxygenation of the mother's blood helps to remedy this deficiency.

Whether these children continue to stay ahead is a matter to watch with close attention. This could prove one of the most significant experiments of our generation.

Gordon Rattray Taylor, *The Biological Time Bomb*

---

unasked. He undertook nothing that wanted initiative, and if asked to do anything he made no response at all.

"He's doing well," Pugh said in the dialect of Argentina.

"He's not. He's turning himself into a machine. Does what he's programmed to do, no reaction to anything else. He's worse off than when he didn't function at all. He's not human any more."

Pugh sighed. "Well, good night," he said in English. "Good night, Kaph."

when somebody says something a person ought to answer. . . ."

The young man looked indifferently in Martin's direction; his eyes still did not seem to see clear through to the person he looked toward. "Why should I answer?"

"Because somebody has said something to you."

"Why?"

Martin shrugged and laughed. Pugh jumped up and turned on the rock-cutter.

Later on he said, "Lay off that, please, Martin."

"Manners are essential in small isolated crews, some kind of manners, whatever you work out together. He's been taught that, everybody in Far Out knows it. Why does he deliberately flout it?"

"Do you tell yourself good night?"

"So?"

"Don't you see Kaph's never known anyone but himself?"

Martin brooded and then broke out, "Then by God this cloning business is all wrong. It won't do. What are a lot of duplicate geniuses going to do for us when they don't even know we exist?"

Pugh nodded. "It might be wiser to separate the clones and bring them up with others. But they make such a grand team this way."

"Do they? I don't know. If this lot had been ten average inefficient ET engineers, would they all have been in the same place at the same time? Would they all have got killed? What if, when the quake came and things started caving in, what if all those kids ran the same way, farther into the mine, maybe, to save the one that was farthest in? Even Kaph was outside and went in. . . . It's hypothetical. But I keep thinking, out of ten ordinary confused guys, more might have got out."

"I don't know. It's true that identical twins tend to die at about the same time, even when they have never seen each other. Identity and death, it is very strange. . . ."

The days went on, the red sun crawled across the dark sky, Kaph did not speak when spoken to, Pugh and Martin snapped at each other more frequently each day. Pugh complained of Martin's snoring. Offended, Martin moved his cot clear across the dome and also ceased speaking to Pugh for some while. Pugh whistled Welsh dirges until Martin complained, and then Pugh stopped speaking for a while.

The day before the Mission ship was due, Martin announced he was going over to Merioneth.

"I thought at least you'd be giving me a hand with the computer to finish the rock-analyses," Pugh said, aggrieved.

"Kaph can do that. I want one more look at the Trench. Have fun," Martin added in dialect, and laughed, and left.

"What is that language?"

"Argentinean. I told you that once, didn't I?"

"I don't know." After a while the young man added, "I have forgotten a lot of things, I think."

"It wasn't important, to be sure," Pugh said gently, realizing all at once how important this conversation was. "Will you give me a hand running the computer, Kaph?"

He nodded.

Pugh had left a lot of loose ends, and the job took them all day. Kaph was a good co-worker, quick and systematic, much more so than Pugh himself. His flat voice, now that he was talking again, got on the nerves; but it didn't matter, there was only this one day left to get through and then the ship would come, the old crew, comrades and friends.

During tea-break Kaph said, "What will happen if the Explorer ship crashes?"

"They'd be killed."

"To you, I mean."

"To us? We'd radio SOS all signals, and live on half rations till the rescue cruiser from Area Three Base came. Four and a half E-years away it is. We have life-support here for three men for, let's see, maybe between four and five years. A bit tight, it would be."

"Would they send a cruiser for three men?"

"They would."

Kaph said no more.

"Enough cheerful speculations," Pugh said cheerfully, rising to get back to work. He slipped sideways and the chair avoided his hand; he did a sort of half-pirouette and fetched up hard against the dome-hide. "My goodness," he said, reverting to his native idiom, "what is it?"

"Quake," said Kaph.

The teacups bounced on the table with a plastic cackle, a litter of papers slid off a box, the skin of the dome swelled and sagged. Underfoot there was a huge noise, half sound half shaking, a subsonic boom.

Kaph sat unmoved. An earthquake does not frighten a man who died in an earthquake.

Pugh, white-faced, wiry black hair sticking out, a frightened man, said, "Martin is in the Trench."

"What trench?"

"The big fault line. The epicenter for the local quakes. Look at the seismograph." Pugh struggled with the stuck door of a still-jittering locker.

"Where are you going?"

"After him."

"Martin took the jet. Sleds aren't safe to use during quakes. They go out of control."

"For God's sake, man, shut up."

Kaph stood up, speaking in a flat voice as usual.

"It's unnecessary to go out after him now. It's taking an unnecessary risk."

"If his alarm goes off, radio me," Pugh said, shut the headpiece of his suit, and ran to the lock. As he went out Libra picked up her ragged skirts and danced a belly-dance from under his feet clear to the red horizon.

Inside the dome, Kaph saw the sled go up, tremble like a meteor in the dull red daylight, and vanish to the northeast. The hide of the dome quivered; the earth coughed. A vent south of the dome belched up a slow-flowing bile of black gas.

A bell shrilled and a red light flashed on the central control board. The sign under the light read Suit Two and scribbled under that, A.G.M. Kaph did not turn the signal off. He tried to radio Martin, then Pugh, but got no reply from either.

The Russians in general have more seriously regarded telepathic studies than has the "Establishment" of American scientists. The Russians are willing even to pay government money on it as a branch of *military* research. In the work at the Bioinformation Institute in Moscow a very definite bias in telepathy toward *visual* rather than linguistic transmission has also been noted. For example, one of the most easily identifiable messages was that of a piece of candy twisted up in brown paper. In general, when a message was attempted, it was what Dr. I.M. Kogan (of the Popov Institute for the Study of Radio Electronics in Moscow) called the "attributes" (the visual peculiarities) that were received rather than the symbolic meaning. A screw driver was received as a "long black-ish-handle sort of thing," not as a specific tool. The tele-pathic sense quite evidently is a survivor of prehistoric eye-mindedness rather than a symbol-sensing development of modern man.

D.E. Carr, *The Forgotten Senses*

When the aftershocks decreased he went back to work, and finished up Pugh's job. It took him about two hours. Every half hour he tried to contact Suit One, and got no reply, then Suit Two and got no reply. The red light had stopped flashing after an hour.

It was dinnertime. Kaph cooked dinner for one, and ate it. He lay down on his cot.

The aftershocks had ceased except for faint rolling tremors at long intervals. The sun hung in the west, oblate, pale-red, immense. It did not sink visibly. There was no sound at all.

Kaph got up and began to walk about the messy, half-packed-up, overcrowded, empty dome. The silence continued. He went to the player and put on the first tape that came to hand. It was pure music, electronic, without harmonies, without voices. It ended. The silence continued.

Pugh's uniform tunic, one button missing, hung over a stack of rock-samples. Kaph stared at it a while.

The silence continued.

The child's dream: There is no one else alive in the world but me. In all the world.

Low, north of the dome, a meteor flickered.

Kaph's mouth opened as if he were trying to say something, but no sound came. He went hastily to the north wall and peered out into the gelatinous red light.

The little star came in and sank. Two figures blurred the airlock. Kaph stood close beside the lock as they came in. Martin's imsuit was covered with some kind of dust so that he looked raddled and warty like the surface of Libra. Pugh had him by the arm.

"Is he hurt?"

Pugh shucked his suit, helped Martin peel off his. "Shaken up," he said, curt.

"A piece of cliff fell onto the jet," Martin said, sitting down at the table and waving his arms. "Not while I was in it, though. I was parked, see, and poking about that carbon-dust area when I felt things humping. So I went out onto a nice bit of early igneous I'd noticed from above, good footing and out from under the cliffs. Then I saw this bit of the planet fall off onto the flyer, quite a sight it was, and after a while it occurred to me the spare aircans were in the flyer, so I leaned on the panic button. But I didn't get any radio reception, that's always happening here during quakes, so I didn't know if the signal was getting through either. And things went on jumping around and pieces of the cliff coming off. Little rocks flying around, and so dusty you couldn't see a meter ahead. I was really beginning to wonder what I'd do for breathing in the small hours, you know, when I saw old Owen buzzing up the Trench in all that dust and junk like a big ugly bat—"

"Want to eat?" said Pugh.

"Of course I want to eat. How'd you come through the quake here, Kaph? No damage? It wasn't a big one actually, was it, what's the seismo say? My trouble was I was in the middle of it. Old Epicenter Alvaro. Felt like Richter Fifteen there—total destruction of planet—"

"Sit down," Pugh said. "Eat."

After Martin had eaten a little his spate of talk ran dry. He very soon went off to his cot, still in the remote angle where he had removed it when Pugh complained of his snoring. "Good night, you one-lunged Welshman," he said across the dome.

When one's customary ways of orienting oneself are threatened, and one is without other selves around one, one is thrown back on inner resources and inner strength, and this is what modern people have neglected to develop.

Rollo May, *Man's Search for Himself*

"Good night."

There was no more out of Martin. Pugh opaqued the dome, turned the lamp down to a yellow glow less than a candle's light, and sat doing nothing, saying nothing, withdrawn.

The silence continued.

"I finished the computations."

Pugh nodded thanks.

"The signal from Martin came through, but I couldn't contact you or him."

Pugh said with effort, "I should not have gone. He had two hours of air left even with only one can. He might have been heading home when I left. This way we were all out of touch with one another. I was scared."

The silence came back, punctuated now by Martin's long, soft snores.

"Do you love Martin?"

Pugh looked up with angry eyes: "Martin is my friend. We've worked together, he's a good man." He stopped. After a while he said, "Yes, I love him. Why did you ask that?"

Kaph said nothing, but he looked at the other man. His face was changed, as if he were glimpsing something he had not seen before; his voice too was changed. "How can you . . . ? How do you . . . ?"

But Pugh could not tell him. "I don't know," he said, "it's practice, partly. I don't know. We're each of us alone, to be sure. What can you do but hold your hand out in the dark?"

Kaph's strange gaze dropped, burned out by its own intensity.

"I'm tired," Pugh said. "That was ugly, looking for him in all that black dust and muck, and mouths opening and shutting in the ground. . . . I'm going to bed. The ship will be transmitting to us by six or so." He stood up and stretched.

"It's a clone," Kaph said. "The other Exploit team they're bringing with them."

"Is it, then?"

"A twelveclone. They came out with us on the *Passerine.*"

Kaph sat in the small yellow aura of the lamp seeming to look past it at what he feared: the new clone, the multiple self of which he was not part. A lost piece of a broken set, a fragment, inexpert at solitude, not knowing even how you go about giving love to another individual, now he must face the absolute, closed self-sufficiency of the clone of twelve; that was a lot to ask of the poor fellow, to be sure. Pugh put a hand on his shoulder in passing. "The chief won't ask you to stay here with a clone. You can go home. Or since you're Far Out maybe you'll come on farther out with us. We could use you. No hurry deciding. You'll make out all right."

Pugh's quiet voice trailed off. He stood unbuttoning his coat, stooped a little with fatigue. Kaph looked at him and saw the thing he had never seen before: saw him: Owen Pugh, the other, the stranger who held his hand out in the dark.

"Good night," Pugh mumbled, crawling into his sleeping-bag and half asleep already, so that he did not hear Kaph reply after a pause, repeating, across darkness, benediction.

You know, whatever is best or greatest in art, science, religion, music, and even sometimes in statesmanship—the great break-throughs are often the result of randomly occurring altered states of consciousness. It was in a vision of a snake eating its own tail that Kekule perceived the atomic binding of the benzene ring, a concept that lies at the basis of biochemistry. Mohammed and his angel, Einstein and relativity. The question arises: These are randomly occurring altered states; what can happen if man can learn to control these, to play at will upon the vast spectrum of consciousness to accomplish certain types of tasks? If we could do this, we would have access to a humanity of such depth and richness as the world has not yet known, so that our great-great grandchildren may look back upon us as Neanderthals, so different will they be.

R.E. Masters and J. Houston, *The Varieties of Postpsychedelic Experience*

The Well
Luis Palés Matos

My soul is like a well of water, quiet, deep,
Within whose solemn and imperturbable peace
The days roll by, with all their worldly murmur stilled,
Like something drowned within the silent cavity.

Down deep, the water cries its bright-hued agony,
A morbid iridescence that in gloom ferments
As it coagulates in blackened trails of slime
And then exhales in phosphorescence, bloodless, blue.

My soul, I say, is like a well. The sleeping world
Takes blurred and obscure form in it, then fades away.
Down low, within the depths perhaps of centuries,
A crouching misanthropic frog hides, lost in dreams.

Sometimes, under the influence of the far-off moon,
The well seems to take on a legendary spell.
One hears the deep croak-croak of the frog within the well
Which then assumes a feeling of eternity.

Master Lü-tsu said, Yü Ch'ing has left behind him a
magic spell for the far journey:

Four words crystallize the spirit in the space of energy.
In the sixth month white snow is suddenly seen to fly.
At the third watch the sun's disk sends out blinding rays.
In the water blows the wind of the Gentle.
Wandering in heaven, one eats the spirit-energy of the Receptive.
And the still deeper secret of the secret:
The land that is nowhere, that is the true home . . .

Richard Wilhelm, tr.,
The Secret of the Golden Flower

For knowledge is the best gift of God to man, to know what is the root and principle of all things. The primal truth is not a body, but it is One, One Truth, One Unity. All things come from it and through it receive truth and unity in the perpetual movement of generation and corruption. There is a hierarchy in things, and lower things are raised to higher things; and higher things descend to lower things. Man is a little world reflecting the great world of the cosmos, but through his intellect the wise man can raise himself above the seven heavens.

Frances A. Yates, *Giordano Bruno and the Hermetic Tradition*

Outlook
Archibald Lampman

Not to be conquered by these headlong days,
But to stand free: to keep the mind at brood
On life's deep meaning, nature's altitude
Of loveliness, and time's mysterious ways;
At every thought and deed to clear the haze
Out of our eyes, considering only this,
What man, what life, what love, what beauty is,
This is to live, and win the final praise.
Though strife, ill fortune, and harsh human need
Beat down the soul, at moments blind and dumb
With agony; yet, patience—there shall come
Many great voices from life's outer sea,
Hours of strange triumph, and, when few men heed,
Murmurs and glimpses of eternity.

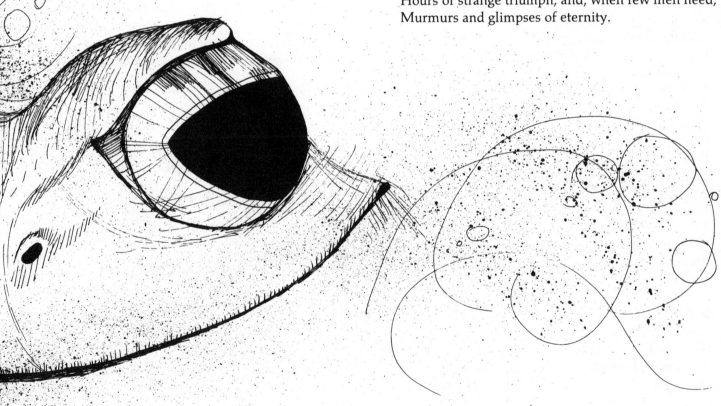

I came back from those holiest waters new, remade, reborn, like a sun-wakened tree that spreads new foliage to the spring dew in sweet freshness, healed of winter's scars; perfect, pure, and ready for the Stars.

Danté, *The Divine Comedy, Purgatorio*

Only giants can save the world from complete relapse and so we—we who care for civilization —have to become giants. We have to bind a harder, stronger civilization like steel about the world.

H.G. Wells, *The Croquet Player*

Letter to Thomas Butts
William Blake

With happiness stretch'd across the hills
In a cloud that dewy sweetness distills,
With a blue sky spread over with wings
And a mild sun that mounts & sings,
With trees & fields full of Fairy elves
And little devils who fight for themselves—
Rememb'ring the Verses that Hayley sung
When my heart knock'd against the root of my tongue—
With Angels planted in Hawthorn bowers
And God himself in the passing hours,
With Silver Angels across my way
And Golden Demons that none can stay,
With my Father hovering upon the wind
And my Brother Robert just behind
And my Brother John, the evil one,
In a black cloud making his mone;
Tho' dead, they appear upon my path,
Notwithstanding my terrible wrath:
They beg, they intreat, they drop their tears,
Fill'd full of hopes, fill'd full of fears—
With a thousand Angels upon the Wind
Pouring disconsolate from behind
To drive them off, & before my way
A frowning Thistle implores my stay.
What to others a trifle appears
Fills me full of smiles or tears;
For double the vision my Eyes do see,
And a double vision is always with me.
With my inward Eye 'tis an old Man grey;
With my outward, a Thistle across my way.
"If thou goest back," the thistle said,
"Thou art to endless woe betray'd;
For here does Theotormon lower
And here is Enitharmon's bower
And Los the terrible thus hath sworn,
Because thou backward dost return,
Poverty, Envy, old age & fear
Shall bring thy Wife upon a bier;
And Butts shall give what Fuseli gave,
A dark black Rock & a gloomy Cave."

I struck the Thistle with my foot,
And broke him up from his delving root:
"Must the duties of life each other cross?
Must every joy be dung & dross?
Must my dear Butts feel cold neglect
Because I give Hayley his due respect?
Must Flaxman look upon me as wild,
And all my friends be with doubts beguil'd?
Must my Wife live in my Sister's bane,
Or my Sister survive on my Love's pain?
The curses of Los, the terrible shade,
And his dismal terrors make me afraid."

So I spoke & struck in my wrath
The old man weltering upon my path.
Then Los appear'd in all his power:
In the Sun he appear'd, descending before
My face in fierce flames; in my double sight
'Twas outward a Sun, inward Los in his might.

"My hands are labour'd day & night,
And Ease comes never in my sight.
My Wife has no indulgence given
Except what comes to her from heaven.
We eat little, we drink less;
This Earth breeds not our happiness.
Another Sun feeds our life's streams,
We are not warmed with thy beams;
Thou measurest not the Time to me,
Nor yet the Space that I do see;
My Mind is not with thy light array'd,
Thy terrors shall not make me afraid."

When I had my Defiance given,
The Sun stood trembling in heaven;
The Moon that glow'd remote below,
Became leprous & white as snow;
And every soul of men on the Earth
Felt affliction & sorrow & sickness & dearth.
Los flam'd in my path, & the Sun was hot
With the bows of my Mind & the Arrows of Thought—
My bowstring fierce with Ardour breathes,
My arrows glow in their golden sheaves;
My brother & father march before;
The heavens drop with human gore.

Now I a fourfold vision see,
And a fourfold vision is given to me;
'Tis fourfold in my supreme delight
And threefold in soft Beulah's night
And twofold Always. May God us keep
From Single vision & Newton's sleep!

The goal is for ever within us; the dream also is within; and the splendour, the meaning, the charm, the witchery, the enchantment, the depth, the height, the distance, are all in a sense within us; for the so-called material universe is only a stage of the soul's advancement in the development of her infinite self.

It is no sea thou seest in the sea,
'Tis but a disguised humanity . . .
All that interests a man *is* man.

At a higher stage, a higher symbolism, a wider universe, a deeper meaning, an increased joy, an intensified loveliness, till the supreme spirit in the full possession of itself, having achieved its own creation, shall enter the Summer Land of eternal maturity, the New Jerusalem, the beatific vision, the higher consciousness of Nirvana.

Arthur Edward Waite, *Azoth; or, the Star in the East*

The Ox and the Man Both Gone Out of Sight

All confusion is set aside, and serenity alone prevails; even the idea of holiness
does not obtain. He does not linger about where the Buddha is,
and as to where there is no Buddha he speedily passes by. When there exists
no form of dualism, even a thousand-eyed one fails to detect a loop-
hole. Who can ever survey the vastness of heaven?

Returning to the Origin, Back to the Source

The man watches the growth of things, while himself abiding in immovable serenity.
Sitting alone, he observes things undergoing changes. To return
to the Origin, to be back at the Source—already a false step this! Far better it is to
stay at home, blind and deaf, and without much ado; sitting in
the hut, he takes no cognisance of things outside, behold the streams
flowing—whither nobody knows; and the flowers vividly red—
for whom are they?

Miracles
Walt Whitman

Why, who makes much of a miracle?
As to me I know of nothing else but miracles,
Whether I walk the streets of Manhattan,
Or dart my sight over the roofs of houses toward the sky,
Or wade with naked feet along the beach just in the edge of the water,
Or stand under trees in the woods,
Or talk by day with anyone I love, or sleep in the bed at night with anyone I love,
Or sit at table at dinner with the rest,
Or look at strangers opposite me riding in the car,
Or watch honey-bees busy around the hive of a summer forenoon,
Or animals feeding in the fields,
Or birds, or the wonderfulness of insects in the air,
Or the wonderfulness of the sundown, or of stars shining so
   quiet and bright,
Or the exquisite delicate thin curve of the new moon in spring;
These with the rest, one and all, are to me miracles,
The whole referring, yet each distinct and in its place.

To me every hour of the light and dark is a miracle,
Every cubic inch of space is a miracle,
Every square yard of the surface of the earth is spread with the same,
Every foot of the interior swarms with the same.

To me the sea is a continual miracle,
The fishes that swim—the rocks—the motion of the waves—the
   ships with men in them,
What stranger miracles are there?

Evolution through Man is tending to a harmonized collectivity of consciousness, equivalent to a kind of superconsciousness. The earth is covering itself not merely with millions of thinking units, but with a single continuum of thought, and finally forming a functionally single Unit of Thought of planetary dimensions. The plurality of individual thoughts combine ... in a single act of unanimous Thought ... In the dimension of Thought, like the dimension of Time and Space, can the Universe reach consummation in anything but the Measureless?

Teilhard de Chardin

... each one of us is potentially Mind at Large. But insofar as we are animals our business is at all costs to survive. To make biological survival possible, Mind at Large has to be funnelled through the reducing valve of the brain and nervous system. What comes out at the other end is a measly trickle of the kind of consciousness which will help us to stay alive on the surface of this particular planet. To formulate and express the contents of this reduced awareness man has invented and endlessly elaborated those symbol-systems and implicit philosophies that we call languages. Every individual is at once the beneficiary and the victim of the linguistic tradition into which he has been born–the beneficiary inasmuch as language gives access to the accumulated records of other people's experience, the victim insofar as it confirms him in the belief that reduced awareness is the only awareness, and as it bedevils his sense of reality, so that he is all too apt to take his concepts for data, his words for actual things. That which, in the language of religion, is called "this world" is the universe of reduced awareness expressed and, as it were, petrified by language. The various "other worlds" with which human beings erratically make contact are so many elements in the totality of awareness belonging to Mind at Large. Most people most of the time know only what comes through the reducing valve and is consecrated as genuinely real by their local language. Certain persons, however seem to be born with a kind of bypass that circumvents the reducing valve. In others temporary bypasses may be acquired either spontaneously or as the result of deliberate "spiritual exercises" or through hypnosis or by means of drugs. Through these permanent or temporary bypasses there flows, not indeed the perception "of everything that is happening everywhere in the universe" . . . but something more than, and above all something different from, the carefully selected, utilitarian material our narrow individual minds regard as a complete, or at least sufficient, picture of reality.

Aldous Huxley, *The Doors of Perception*

The Alchemical Hill
Stuart Mackinnon

For a unity that was never jagged,
for a simplicity that was folded
neatly about the pronouns of my childhood
stands the alchemical hill in the sunlight
traversed by the road I rarely travelled.

Instead I daily turned at the bottom
and skirted the clean flank
by a dusty road beside leaden stones.
At evening when the sun would surround it
I was tired and obliquely satisfied.

Once with my father we clattered
down in a rattling car and fired
up the opposite hill and that was fun
one evening. But never, never in
the morning alone or still.

Although much later I mapped and surveyed it
and made it a subject of topographical skill;
too late–too soon its meaning comes to me
that it was the one and sum of all the hills.

And I do think that man is related to the universe in some 'religious' way even prior to his relations to his fellow men. And I do think that the only way of true relationship between men is to meet in some common 'belief', but physical not mental . . . There is a principle in the universe towards which man turns religiously–a life of the universe itself. And the hero is he who touches and transmits the life of the universe . . .

D.H. Lawrence, *Letters of D.H. Lawrence*

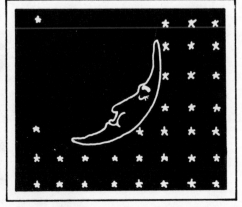

Cinderella
Sandra McPherson

When she came to the mirror it was to her
Instrument of change, every scene in it
Total background, and her hard looking
Asking only to be plumbed the depth
Of a diamond needle, the broken in her
Still breakable as if new. A red line rose
And fell between images of dawn
And sunset . . .

            This was the dream room,
That had been lived with and never opened.
Everything in it was imagined, the curtains
The color of Chinese skin, with large printed
Purple blooms like distant ferris wheels
At dusk. At night the stars used themselves
Up on the rug.

            Footsteps sounded
Into many years. Now someone enters
By the window. She turns, quiet.
The temperature drops. On the sill she finds
The alchemical gold ginkgo leaf and it fits
Perfectly the foot that she puts down
Gently on the beginning of autumn.

Lirazel Blows Away
Lord Dunsany

And the days went by, the Summer passed over Erl, the sun that had travelled northward fared South again, it was near to the time when the swallows left those eaves, and Lirazel had not learnt anything. She had not prayed to the stars again, or supplicated their images, but she had learned no human customs, and could not see why her love and gratitude must remain unexpressed to the stars. And Alveric did not know that the time must come when some simple trivial thing would divide them utterly.

And then one day, hoping still, he took her with him to the house of the Freer to teach her how to worship his holy things. And gladly the good man brought his candle and bell, and the eagle of brass that held up his book when he read, and a little symbolic bowl that had scented water, and the silver snuffers that put his candle out. And he told her clearly and simply, as he had told her before, the origin, meaning and mystery of all these things, and why the bowl was of brass and the snuffer of silver, and what the symbols were that were carved on the bowl. With fitting courtesy he told her these things, even with kindness; and yet there was something in his voice as he told, a little distant from her; and she knew that he spoke as one that walked safe on shore calling far to a mermaid amid dangerous seas.

As they came back to the castle the swallows were grouped to go, sitting in lines along the battlements. And Lirazel had promised to worship the holy things of the Freer, like the simple bell-fearing folk of the valley of Erl: and a late hope was shining in Alveric's mind that even yet all was well. And for many days she remembered all that the Freer had told her.

And one day walking late from the nursery, past tall windows to her tower, and looking out on the evening, remembering that she must not worship the stars, she called to mind the holy things of the Freer, and tried to remember all she was told of them. It seemed so hard to worship them just as she should. She knew that before many hours the swallows would all be gone; and often when they left her her mood would change; and she feared that she might forget, and never remember more, how she ought to worship the holy things of the Freer.

So she went out into the night again over the grasses to where a thin brook ran, and drew out some great flat pebbles that she knew where to find, turning her face away from the images of the stars. By day the stones shone beautifully in the water, all ruddy and mauve; now they were all dark. She drew them out and laid them in the meadow: she loved these smooth flat stones, for somehow they made her remember the rocks of Elfland.

She laid them all in a row, this for the candlestick, this for the bell, that for the holy bowl. "If I can worship these lovely stones as things ought to be worshipped," she said, "I can worship the things of the Freer."

Then she kneeled down before the big flat stones and prayed to them as though they were Christom things.

And Alveric seeking her in the wide night, wondering what wild fancy had carried her whither, heard her voice in the meadow, crooning such prayers as are offered to holy things.

When he saw the four flat stones to which she prayed, bowed down before them in the grass, he said that no worse than this were the darkest ways of the heathen. And she said "I am learning to worship the holy things of the Freer."

"It is the art of the heathen," he said.

Now of all things that men feared in the valley of Erl they feared most the arts of the heathen, of whom they knew nothing but that their ways were dark. And he spoke with the anger which men always used when they spoke there of the heathen. And his anger went to her heart, for she was but learning to worship his holy things to please him, and yet he had spoken like this.

And Alveric would not speak the words that should have been said, to turn aside anger and soothe her; for no man, he foolishly thought, should compro-

mise in matters touching on heathenesse. So Lirazel went alone all sadly back to her tower. And Alveric stayed to cast the four flat stones afar.

And the swallows left, and unhappy days went by. And one day Alveric bade her worship the holy things of the Freer, and she had quite forgotten how. And he spoke again of the arts of heathenesse. The day was shining and the poplars golden and all the aspens red.

Then Lirazel went to her tower and opened the casket, that shone in the morning with the clear autumnal light, and took in her hand the rune of the King of Elfland, and carried it with her across the high vaulted hall, and came to another tower and climbed its steps to the nursery.

And there all day she stayed and played with her child, with the scroll still tight in her hand: and, merrily though she played at whiles, yet there were strange calms in her eyes, which Ziroonderel watched while she wondered. And when the sun was low and she had put the child to bed she sat beside him all solemn as she told him childish tales. And Ziroonderel, the wise witch, watched; and for all her wisdom only guessed how it would be, and knew not how to make it otherwise.

And before sunset Lirazel kissed the boy and unrolled the Elf King's scroll. It was but a petulance that had made her take it from the coffer in which it lay, and the petulance might have passed and she might not have unrolled the scroll, only that it was there in her hand. Partly petulance, partly wonder, partly whims too idle to name, drew her eyes to the Elf King's words in their coal-black curious characters.

And whatever magic there was in the rune of which I cannot tell (and dreadful magic there was), the rune was written with love that was stronger than magic, till those mystical characters glowed with the love that the Elf King had for his daughter, and there were blended in that mighty rune two powers, magic and love, the greatest power there is beyond the boundary of twilight with the greatest power there is in the fields we know. And if Alveric's love could have held her he should have trusted alone to that love, for the Elf King's rune was mightier than the holy things of the Freer.

No sooner had Lirazel read the rune on the scroll than fancies from Elfland began to pour over the border. Some came that would make a clerk in the City to-day leave his desk at once to dance on the sea-shore; and some would have driven all the men in a bank to leave doors and coffers open and wander away till they came to green open land and the heathery hills; and some would have made a poet of a man, all of a sudden as he sat at his business. They were mighty fancies that the Elf King summoned by the force of his magical rune. And Lirazel sat there with the rune in her hand, helpless amongst this mass of tumultuous fancies from Elfland. And as the fancies raged and sang and called, more and more over the border, all crowding on one poor mind, her body grew lighter and lighter. Her feet half rested half floated, upon the floor; Earth scarcely held her down, so fast was she becoming a thing of dreams. No love of hers for Earth, or of the children of Earth for her, had any longer power to hold her there.

And now came memories of her ageless childhood beside the tarns of Elfland, by the deep forest's border, by those delirious lawns, or in the palace that may not be told of except only in song. She saw those things as clearly as we see small shells in water, looking through clear ice down to the floor of some sleeping lake, a little dimmed in that other region across the barrier of ice; so too her memories shone a little dimly from across the frontier of Elfland. Little queer sounds of elfin creatures came to her, scents swam from those miraculous flowers that glowed by the lawns she knew, faint sounds of enchanted songs blew over the border and reached her seated there, voices and melodies and memories came floating through the twilight, all Elfland was calling. Then measured and resonant, and strangely near, she heard her father's voice.

She rose at once, and now Earth had lost on her the grip that it only has on material things, and a thing of dreams and fancy and fable and phantasy she drifted from the room; and Ziroonderel had no power to hold her with any spell, nor had she herself the power even to turn, even to look at her boy as she drifted away.

And at that moment a wind came out of the north-west, and entered the woods and bared the golden branches, and danced on over the downs, and led a company of scarlet and golden leaves, that had dreaded this day but danced now it had come; and away with a riot of dancing and glory of colour, high in the light of the sun that had set from the sight of the fields, went wind and leaves together. With them went Lirazel.

Our normal waking consciousness, rational consciousness as we call it, is but one special type of consciousness, whilst all about it, parted from it by the finest of screens, there lie potential forms of consciousness entirely different. We may go through life without suspecting their existence; but apply the requisite stimulus, and at a touch they are there in all completeness, definite types of mentality which probably somewhere have their field of application and adaptation. No account of the universe in its totality can be final which leaves these other forms of consciousness quite disregarded. How to regard them is the question,- for they are so discontinuous with ordinary consciousness. Yet they may determine attitudes though they cannot furnish formulas, and open a region though they fail to give a map. At any rate they forbid a premature closing of our accounts with reality.

William James, *The Principles of Psychology*

The Inward Angel
Jay Macpherson

A diamond self, more clear and hard
Than breath can cloud or touch can stain,
About my wall keeps mounted guard,
Maintaining an impervious reign.

But planted as an inward eye
And nourishing my patient mold,
He's soft with sense, and round him I
Ingather sun where all was cold.

Look, inward Angel, cast your light:
My dark is crystal in your sight.

We and the cosmos are one. The cosmos is a vast living body, of which we are still parts. The sun is a great heart whose tremors run through our smallest veins. The moon is a great gleaming nerve-centre from which we quiver forever. Who knows the power that Saturn has over us or Venus? But it is a vital power, rippling exquisitely through us *all the time*. . . .

Now all this is literally true, as men knew in the great past and as they will know again.

D.H. Lawrence, *Apocalypse*

"I was sitting on the seashore, half listening to a friend arguing violently about something which merely bored me. Unconsciously to myself, I looked at a film of sand I had picked up on my hand, when I suddenly saw the exquisite beauty of every little grain of it; instead of being dull, I saw that each particle was made up on a perfect geometrical pattern, with sharp angles, from each of which a brilliant shaft of light was reflected, while each tiny crystal shone like a rainbow ... The rays crossed and recrossed, making exquisite patterns of such beauty that they left me breathless. ... Then, suddenly, my consciousness was lighted up from within and I saw in a vivid way how the whole universe was made up of particles of material which, no matter how dull and life-less they might seem, were nevertheless filled with this intense and vital beauty. For a second or two the whole world appeared as a blaze of glory. When it died down, it left me with something I have never forgotten and which constantly reminds me of the beauty locked up in every minute speck of material around us."

Aldous Huxley, *The Doors of Perception*

from The God of the Labyrinth
Colin Wilson

. . . And now it struck me that all that matters in human existence is a certain intensity of consciousness, of meaning, and that we must discover the trick. When I bought this car, it had an automatic choke, and the damned thing would cut out almost as soon as I began driving, so that the engine would stop on the first hill into town. So our local garage fixed an ordinary hand-choke instead, and now I keep it out until the engine is warm enough to take the hills comfortably. But if I wake up in the morning with my mind cold and dull, there is no mental choke I can pull out until the engine is heated up. I often spend hours, or even days, trying to cudgel my brains into a state of intensity, trying to work up the inner-pressure to settle down to writing. To some extent, I have discovered the trick: ten minutes of intense, total concentration, involving the whole being—my muscles as well as my brain. As I do this—if no one interrupts me—I can almost watch the pressure of my consciousness rising. Until things no longer seem dull and neutral. It is exactly like having your first drink of the evening—that warm glow that is not situated in the stomach, but *in consciousness*.

And now the strange thing happened—a thing I cannot possibly convey to the reader, but which I can at least try to describe. The thought came to me that this was how Esmond had felt as he set out on his *wanderjahre* in 1765. And then two images fused together in my mind. One was of Esmond setting off in the coach from Limerick—something I had dreamed about in the night. The other was the image of the trees on Long Island suddenly looking as if they were cast out of phosphor bronze, as Beverley bent over me. This latter image was very strong. I could smell Beverley's scent, feel the warmth of her bare breast against my cheek. And with these two images came an explosion of delight. What human beings want is to achieve these moments of freshness and intensity, and not to lose them every time their attention wanders. They want *continuity of consciousness*. And supposing a man said to himself: "It is obvious that nothing is as important as this: from now on I shall devote my life to the search for this intensity and continuity . . . "? And I knew beyond all possible doubt, that something like this had passed through Esmond's mind on that morning drive from Limerick.

How? Because I had lived with Esmond for weeks, until I knew how his mind worked.

And now, without any sudden change, any feeling of vision or inspiration, I had a hallucinatory feeling of *being Esmond*. It was absurdly strong. I knew I was driving through a small hamlet called Fardrum, a few miles beyond Athlone, and that I intended to stop at the pub at Moate for a ham sandwich and a draught Guinness. At the same time, I was seated beside the coachman on the box of a jolting coach, smelling the lathery sweat of the horses and the clean air of an April morning, as well as the tang of peat smoke from the clothes of the driver.

There was something very odd about the vividness of this image. It was not "imaginative" in the ordinary sense: I was not somehow "intending" it. It was as if something had moved close to me, like a train passing the train in which I happened to be sitting, and giving me a sudden intimate glimpse into a passing carriage. And all this did not surprise me. It seemed a natural part of the upsurge of delight. My mental pressure was high. The sky was a rather cool blue, and I felt as though it were an immense sheet of cool water. It struck me with sudden total certainty: time is an illusion. It is not an absolute state. If you are an insect sitting on a leaf that is swept down a river, you might think that it is inevitable that trees keep passing you and receding behind you, that by their very nature trees only last a few moments, and the only unchanging reality is the ripple and splash of the water. But the bank is real, and if you could get off your leaf on to the bank, you would find that it is quite solid and permanent.

As soon as I had this picture of time as something illusory, and of the reality of the world through which it flows, I saw my own childhood as something I could reach out and touch, just as I can open a book to a page I read an hour ago, or make a tape recorder rewind to an earlier part of the tape. And it struck me that Esmond's life was no more distant; a mere two centuries ago, two lifetimes. Our trouble is the feebleness of consciousness, which fluctuates like the electric current from a worn-out battery. If we could replace this with a new battery, the mind could stride across centuries . . .

You are your own creator; you appear
In the splendor of your own.
Heaven and earth are made light by you

Pyramid Text

The Anagogic Man
Jay Macpherson

Noah walks with head bent down;
For between his nape and crown
He carries, balancing with care,
A golden bubble round and rare.

Its gently shimmering sides surround
All us and our worlds, and bound
Art and life, and wit and sense,
Innocence and Experience.

Forbear to startle him, lest some
Poor soul to its destruction come,
Slipped out of mind and past recall
As if it never was at all.

O you that pass, if still he seems
One absent-minded or in dreams,
Consider that your senses keep
A death far deeper than his sleep.

Angel, declare: what sways when Noah nods?
The sun, the stars, the figures of the gods.

from The Transformation
George B. Leonard

It is midnight of the first full moon after the autumnal equinox. An old man stands on a rocky prominence near the east peak of the sacred mountain. He is dressed in battered work shoes, faded khakis and a shabby parka. Above his head he holds a crystal about the size of a soccer ball. His head is flung back so that his eyes and the crystal and the moon are perfectly aligned.

Earlier in the evening this man, the last shaman of the tribe of Indians that once lived on the mountain's slopes, drove south to the mountain from the little town where he makes a living doing odd jobs in the white man's world. He parked his old pickup truck at the end of a dirt road that runs about halfway up the mountain, took out a shovel, and climbed to the crystal's hiding place. He followed no trail, only his sure sense of where it would have to be.

The shaman dug the crystal from the ground, placed it in a gunnysack, and returned to the truck. He drove then to the ocean on the other side of the mountain. He parked near a lonely stretch of beach. He unbuttoned two buttons of his parka and slipped the crystal inside. Cradling it there, he walked out into

the moonlit water where it ebbed and flowed among rugged rocks.

He washed the crystal thoroughly, then, holding it carefully in both hands, approached one of the projecting rocks. Chanting softly, he struck the crystal on the rock four times, each time with increasing force. It was a perilous operation. The shaman knew he had to strike hard enough to jar loose any demon that might be clinging to the crystal. But if he struck too hard the crystal would break, which would bring the world to an end. He was not absolutely sure that would happen. He did know, however, that if the crystal broke he would die in an instant. . . .

The shaman drove back to the mountain and climbed to the prominence. He waited there for the moon to mount to the zenith, then raised the crystal above his head. A faint pulse from the sun, reflecting off the moon, resonated at the precise frequency of the crystal and entered the shaman's very being. He fell into a trance and was transported to the circumference of that sphere where physical distance yields its domain, where past, present and future touch. . . .

At the same time three other men, also shamans of near-extinct tribes, raised their crystals to the moon. They too were standing on sacred mountains. The mountains were many miles apart, the four corners of a great square on this earth. In an instant the four men were joined into a single being. There was in each of them an awareness of all aspects of all of them, aspects we might express as facial expression or smell or sense of humor or essence. But none of this was experienced as separate. No face was separate from another, and "face" was not separate from smell or sound or being. In this joining the great vision of change within the changeless unfolded again.

The shaman was so filled that there was no space left for regret or exaltation. He had seen it before. Those who came before him had seen it. He was an old man. He would probably not see it again on this plane of existence. But that was all right, for it *is:* The passing away of his people's way of life. The coming of the white men. The passing away of their way of life. The coming of something different, long awaited. Was it a way his people might have hoped for? He was not sure. But that is not a question he would ask, for the end may precede the beginning, and beneath every conceivable sky it is always now.

The shaman stands there in my memory, a moonlit statue against the cloudless night.

Why hast thou enticed thyself
Into the old serpent's Paradise?
Why hast thou stolen
Into thyself, thyself? . . .
Encaved within thyself,
Burrowing into thyself . . .
Piled with a hundred burdens . . .
A knower!
Self-knower!
You sought the heaviest burden
And found yourself.

Nietzsche

Without beginning, without end,
Without past, without future.
A halo of light surrounds the world of the law.
We forget one another, quiet and pure, altogether
    powerful and empty.
The emptiness is irradiated by the light of the heart
    and of heaven.
The water of the sea is smooth and mirrors the moon
    in its surface.
The clouds disappear in blue space; the mountains
    shine clear.
Consciousness reverts to contemplation; the moon-
    disk rests alone.

Richard Wilhelm, tr., *The Secret of the Golden Flower*

To escape from a sense of separation, from the loneliness of selfhood, towards a closer participation and reunion with Nature and God, which will bring peace and rest to the soul . . .

This urge has its origin, if one accepts the only thesis on which a case for the validity of mysticism is based, in the fact that man is in some way a sharer in the divine life. He therefore longs to return to that from which he feels he has come, to be more closely and consciously linked with it. He feels himself to be a pilgrim of eternity, a creature in time but a citizen of a timeless world.

Since man is a sharer in the divine life, there is a mutual and reciprocal attraction. The mysticism of love and union can be described not only in terms of man's search for God but also in terms of God's search for man. "I sought for God for thirty years," writes the Moslem mystic Abu Yazid. "I thought it was I who desired Him, but, no, it was He who desired me."

Frank C. Happold, *Mysticism*

Good Friday, 1613. Riding Westward
John Donne

Let man's soul be a sphere, and then, in this,
The intelligence that moves, devotion is,
And as the other spheres, by being grown
Subject to foreign motions, lose their own,
And being by others hurried every day,
Scarce in a year their natural form obey;
Pleasure or business, so, our souls admit
For their first mover, and are whirled by it.
Hence is't, that I am carried towards the West
This day, when my soul's form bends towards the East.
There I should see a Sun, by rising, set,
And by that setting endless day beget:
But that Christ on this cross did rise and fall,
Sin had eternally benighted all.
Yet dare I almost be glad I do not see
That spectacle, of too much weight for me.
Who sees God's face, that is self-life, must die;
What a death were it then to see God die?
It made his own lieutenant, Nature, shrink;
It made his footstool crack, and the sun wink.
Could I behold those hands which span the poles,
And tune all spheres at once, pierced with those holes?
Could I behold that endless height which is
Zenith to us, and our antipodes,
Humbled below us? Or that blood which is
The seat of all our souls, if not of His,
Make dirt of dust, or that flesh which was worn
By God, for his apparel, ragg'd and torn?
If on these things I durst not look, durst I
Upon his miserable mother cast mine eye,
Who was God's partner here, and furnished thus
Half of that sacrifice which ransomed us?
Though these things, as I ride, be from mine eye,
They are present yet unto my memory,
For that looks towards them; and Thou look'st towards me;
O Saviour, as Thou hang'st upon the tree.
I turn my back to Thee but to receive
Corrections, till Thy mercies bid Thee leave.
O think me worth Thine anger; punish me;
Burn off my rusts and my deformity;
Restore Thine image so much, by Thy grace,
That Thou may'st know me, and I'll turn my face.

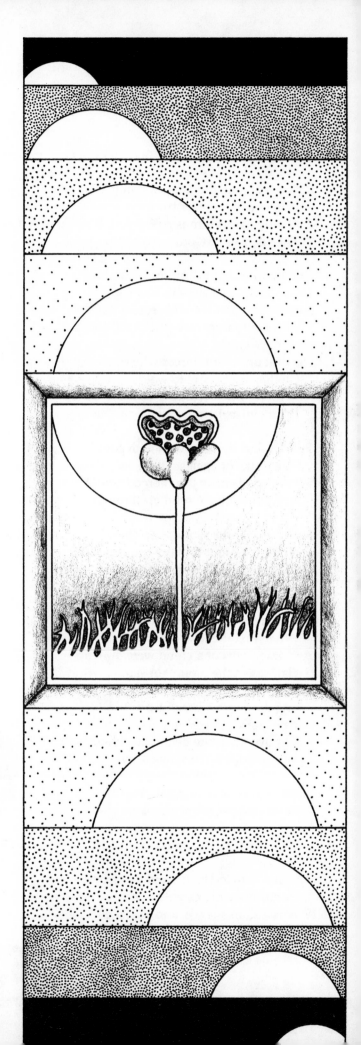

The Unnamed Lake
Frederick George Scott

It sleeps among the thousand hills
   Where no man ever trod,
And only nature's music fills
   The silences of God.

Great mountains tower above its shore,
   Green rushes fringe its brim,
And o'er its breast for evermore
   The wanton breezes skim.

Dark clouds that intercept the sun
   Go there in Spring to weep,
And there, when Autumn days are done,
   White mists lie down to sleep.

Sunrise and sunset crown with gold
   The peaks of ageless stone,
Where winds have thundered from of old
   And storms have set their throne.

No echoes of the world afar
   Disturb it night or day,
But sun and shadow, moon and star
   Pass and repass for aye.

'Twas in the gray of early dawn,
   When first the lake we spied,
And fragments of a cloud were drawn
   Half down the mountain side.

Along the shore a heron flew,
   And from a speck on high,
That hovered in the deepening blue,
   We heard the fish-hawk's cry.

Among the cloud-capt solitudes,
   No sound the silence broke,
Save when, in whispers down the woods,
   The guardian mountains spoke.

Through tangled brush and dewy brake,
   Returning whence we came,
We passed in silence, and the lake
   We left without a name.

Lines: I Praise God's Mankind in an Old Woman
Wilfred Watson

I praise God's mankind in an old woman:
I hear him rattle the body of an old wife
Dry and brown, and bitter as bracken,
Her stalk womb-cancelled, sere with seedgone;
With shrivel fingers clutching upon her life,
Wrestling for the empty pod and the dry leaf.
But still in her mildewed eyes moist's last token—
But oh, ever in her eyes the flash and strife,
Husk edge, cruel and sharp as any knife
Which not God's death itself can unsharpen.
Not all the frosts marching to this last March
Frost, not all the suns flaming to August
The last, dry-dried her spirit to adust;
She her own frost and sun at last must
Fetch—to blaze within and her soul's spirit parch
Into a desert—her own contracted flame;
Her radical sin, this sin at last to tame.
May she like the fathers by the desert broken
In her own desert find at last salvation.

Vestigia
Bliss Carman

I took a day to search for God,
And found Him not. But as I trod
By rocky ledge, through woods untamed,
Just where one scarlet lily flamed,
I saw His footprint in the sod.

Then suddenly, all unaware,
Far off in the deep shadows, where
A solitary hermit thrush
Sang through the holy twilight hush—
I heard His voice upon the air.

And even as I marvelled how
God gives us Heaven here and now,
In a stir of wind that hardly shook
The poplar leaves beside the brook—
His hand was light upon my brow.

At last with evening as I turned
Homeward, and thought what I had learned
And all that there was still to probe—
I caught the glory of His robe
Where the last fires of sunset burned.

Back to the world with quickening start
I looked and longed for any part
In making saving Beauty be—
And from that kindling ecstasy
I knew God dwelt within my heart.

Evensong
Lester del Rey

By the time he reached the surface of the little planet, even the dregs of his power were drained. Now he rested, drawing reluctant strength slowly from the yellow sun that shone on the greensward around him. His senses were dim with an ultimate fatigue, but the fear he had learned from the Usurpers drove them outward, seeking a further hint of sanctuary.

It was a peaceful world, he realized, and the fear thickened in him at the discovery. In his younger days, he had cherished a multitude of worlds where the game of life's ebb and flow could be played to the hilt. It had been a lusty universe to roam then. But the Usurpers could brook no rivals to their own outreaching lust. The very peace and order here meant that this world had once been theirs.

He tested for them gingerly while the merest whisper of strength poured into him. None were here now. He could have sensed the pressure of their close presence at once, and there was no trace of that. The even grassland swept in rolling meadows and swales to the distant hills. There were marble structures in the distance, sparkling whitely in the late sunlight, but they were empty, their unknown purpose altered to no more than decoration now upon this abandoned planet. His attention swept back, across a stream to the other side of the wide valley.

There he found the garden. Within low walls, its miles of expanse were a tree-crowded and apparently untended preserve. He could sense the stirring of larger animal life among the branches and along the winding paths. The brawling vigor of all proper life was missing, but its abundance might be enough to mask his own vestige of living force from more than careful search.

It was at least a better refuge than this open greensward and he longed toward it, but the danger of betraying motion held him still where he was. He had thought his previous escape to be assured, but he was learning that even he could err. Now he waited while he tested once more for evidence of Usurper trap.

He had mastered patience in the confinement the Usurpers had designed at the center of the galaxy. He had gathered his power furtively while he designed escape around their reluctance to make final disposition. Then he had burst outward in a drive that should have thrust him far beyond the limits of their hold on the universe. And he had found failure before he could span even the distance to the end of this spiral arm of one galactic fastness.

Their webs of detection were everywhere, seemingly. Their great power-robbing lines made a net too fine to pass. Stars and worlds were linked, until only a series of miracles had carried him this far. And now the waste of power for such miracles was no longer within his reach. Since their near failure in entrapping and sequestering him, they had learned too much.

Now he searched delicately, afraid to trip some alarm, but more afraid to miss its existence. From space, this world had offered the only hope in its seeming freedom from their webs. But only microseconds had been available to him for his testing then.

At last he drew his perceptions back. He could find no slightest evidence of their lures and detectors here. He had begun to suspect that even his best efforts might not be enough now, but he could do no more. Slowly at first, and then in a sudden rush, he hurled himself into the maze of the garden.

Nothing struck from the skies. Nothing leaped upwards from the planet core to halt him. There was no interruption in the rustling of the leaves and the chirping bird songs. The animal sounds went on unhindered. Nothing seemed aware of his presence in the garden. Once that would have been unthinkable in itself, but now he drew comfort from it. He must be only a shadow self now, unknown and unknowable in his passing.

Something came down the path where he rested, pattering along on hoofs that touched lightly on the spoilage of fallen leaves. Something else leaped quickly through the light underbrush beside the path.

He let his attention rest on them as they both emerged onto the near pathway at once. And cold horror curled thickly around him.

One was a rabbit, nibbling now at the leaves of clover and twitching long ears as its pink nose stretched out for more. The other was a young deer, still bearing the spots of its fawnhood. Either or both might seemingly have been found on any of a thousand worlds. But neither would have been precisely of the type before him.

This was the Meeting World—the planet where he had first found the ancestors of the Usurpers. Of all worlds in the pested galaxy, it had to be *this* world he sought for refuge!

They were savages back in the days of his full glory, confined to this single world, rutting and driving their way to the lawful self-destruction of all such savages. And yet there had been something odd about them, something that then drew his attention and even his vagrant pity.

Out of that pity, he had taught a few of them, and led them upwards. He had even nursed poetic fancies of making them his companions and his equals as the life span of their sun should near its ending. He had answered their cries for help and given them at least some of what they needed to set their steps toward power over even space and energy. And they had rewarded him by overweening pride that denied even a trace of gratitude. He had abandoned them finally to their own savage ends and gone on to other worlds, to play out the purposes of a wider range.

It was his second folly. They were too far along the path toward unlocking the laws behind the universe. Somehow, they even avoided their own destruction from themselves. They took the worlds of their sun and drove outwards, until they could even vie with him for the worlds he had made particularly his own. And now they owned them all, and he had only a tiny spot here on their world—for a time at least.

The horror of the realization that this was the Meeting World abated a little as he remembered now how readily their spawning hordes possessed and abandoned worlds without seeming end. And again the tests he could make showed no evidence of them here. He began to relax again, feeling a sudden hope from what had been temporary despair. Surely they might also believe this was the one planet where he would never seek sanctuary.

Now he set his fears aside and began to force his thoughts toward the only pattern that could offer hope. He needed power, and power was available in any area untouched by the webs of the Usurpers. It had drained into space itself throughout the aeons, a waste of energy that could blast suns or build them in legions. It was power to escape, perhaps even to prepare himself eventually to meet them with at least a chance to force truce, if not victory. Given even a few hours free of their notice, he could draw and hold that power for his needs.

He was just reaching for it when the sky thundered and the sun seemed to darken for a moment!

Jesus said to them: When you make the two one, and when you make the inner as the outer and the outer as the inner and the above as the below, and when you make the male and female into a single one, so that the male will not be male and the female not be female, when you make eyes in the place of an eye, and a hand in the place of a hand, and a foot in the place of a foot, and an image in the place of an image, then shall you enter the kingdom.

The Gospel According to Thomas

The fear in him gibbered to the surface and sent him huddling from sight of the sky before he could control it. But for a brief moment there was still a trace of hope in him. It could have been a phenomenon caused by his own need for power; he might have begun drawing too heavily, too eager for strength.

Then the earth shook, and he knew.

The Usurpers were not fooled. They knew he was here—had never lost him. And now they had followed in all their massive lack of subtlety. One of their scout ships had landed, and the scout would come seeking him.

He fought for control of himself, and found it long enough to drive his fear back down within himself. Now, with a care that disturbed not even a blade of grass or leaf on a twig, he began retreating, seeking the denser undergrowth at the center of the garden where all life was thickest. With that to screen him, he might at least draw a faint trickle of power, a strength to build a subtle brute aura around himself and let him hide among the beasts. Some Usurper scouts were young and immature. Such a one might be fooled into leaving. Then, before his report could be acted on by others, there might be a chance. . . .

He knew the thought was only a wish, not a plan, but he clung to it as he huddled in the thicket at the center of the garden. And then even the fantasy was stripped from him.

The sound of footsteps was firm and sure.

Branches broke as the steps came forward, not deviating from a straight line. Inexorably, each firm stride brought the Usurper nearer to his huddling place. Now there was a faint glow in the air, and the animals were scampering away in terror.

He felt the eyes of the Usurper on him, and he forced himself away from that awareness. And, like fear, he found that he had learned prayer from the Usurpers; he prayed now desperately to a nothingness he knew, and there was no answer.

"Come forth! This earth is a holy place and you cannot remain upon it. Our judgment is done and a place is prepared for you. Come forth and let me take you there!" The voice was soft, but it carried a power that stilled even the rustling of the leaves.

He let the gaze of the Usurper reach him now, and the prayer in him was mute and directed outward—and hopeless, as he knew it must be.

"But—" Words were useless, but the bitterness inside him forced the words to come from him. "But why? I am God!"

For a moment, something akin to sadness and pity was in the eyes of the Usurper. Then it passed as the answer came. "I know. But I am Man. Come!"

He bowed at last, silently, and followed slowly as the yellow sun sank behind the walls of the garden.

And the evening and the morning were the eighth day.

Unless you make yourself equal to God, you cannot understand God: for the like is not intelligible save to the like. Make yourself grow to a greatness beyond measure, by a bound free yourself from the body; raise yourself above all time, become Eternity; then you will understand God. Believe that nothing is impossible for you, think yourself immortal and capable of understanding all, all arts, all sciences, the nature of every living being. Mount higher than the highest height; descend lower than the lowest depth. Draw into yourself all sensations of everything created, fire and water, dry and moist, imagining that you are everywhere, on earth, in the sea, in the sky, that you are not yet born, in the maternal womb, adolescent, old, dead, beyond death. If you embrace in your thought all things at once, times, places, substances, qualities, quantities, you may understand God.

Frances A. Yates,
Giordano Bruno and the Hermetic Tradition

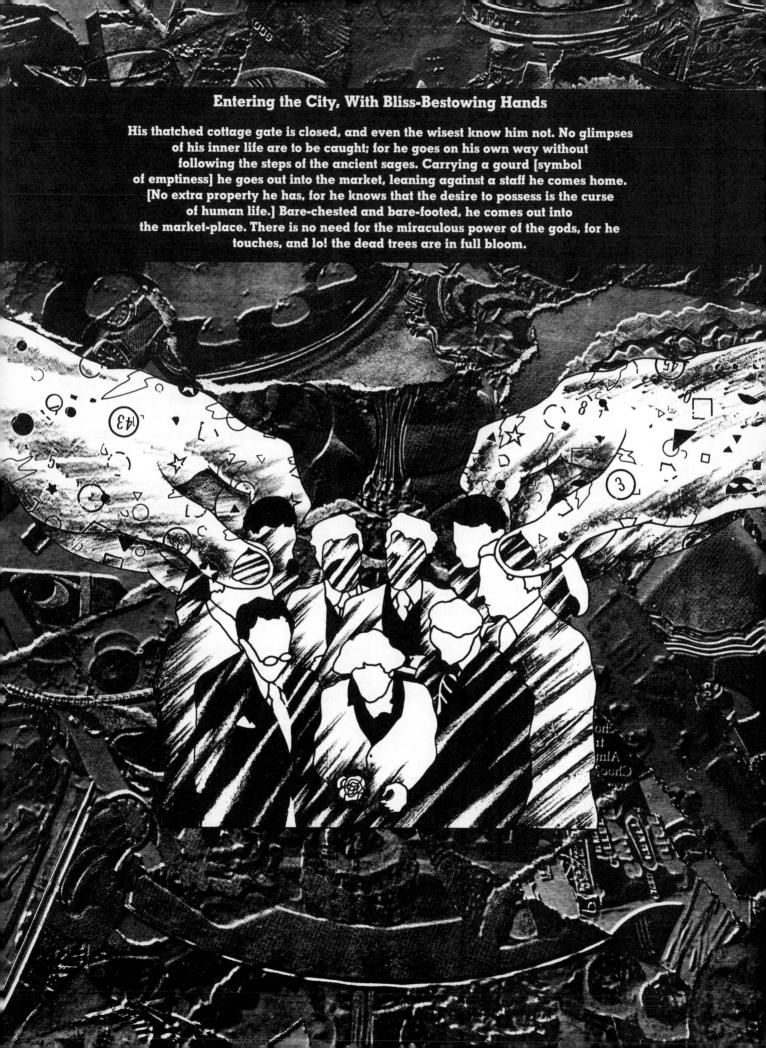

Entering the City, With Bliss-Bestowing Hands

His thatched cottage gate is closed, and even the wisest know him not. No glimpses of his inner life are to be caught; for he goes on his own way without following the steps of the ancient sages. Carrying a gourd [symbol of emptiness] he goes out into the market, leaning against a staff he comes home. [No extra property he has, for he knows that the desire to possess is the curse of human life.] Bare-chested and bare-footed, he comes out into the market-place. There is no need for the miraculous power of the gods, for he touches, and lo! the dead trees are in full bloom.

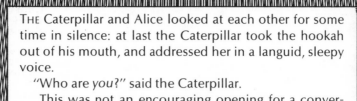

THE Caterpillar and Alice looked at each other for some time in silence: at last the Caterpillar took the hookah out of his mouth, and addressed her in a languid, sleepy voice.

"Who are *you*?" said the Caterpillar.

This was not an encouraging opening for a conversation. Alice replied, rather shyly, "I–I hardly know, Sir, just at present–at least I know who I *was* . . .

Lewis Carroll, *Alice's Adventures in Wonderland*

Illustration Credits

Brant Cowie: 58, 59, 100, 101, 122, 123
Helen Fox: 70, 71
William Fox: 22, 24
Frank Hammond: 82, 83, 106, 137
Emma Hesse: 9, 67, 105, 114, 115, 135
Saul Jaskus: 5, 57, 94
Robert Kebic: 32, 33, 55, 88, 89
Tibor Kovalik: 14, 15, 16, 17, 48, 49, 84, 85
Neil R. McInnes/Audience: 62, 63
Jim McLachlan: 28, 29, 36, 37, 90, 91, 128, 129
David Shaw: 50, 51, 69, 124, 125, 130, 133, 143
David Simmons: 10, 11, 38, 39
Ken Stampnick/Audience: 20, 21, 44, 45, 99
Rene Zamic: 1, 2, 3, 7, 26, 27, 30, 31, 34, 35, 60, 61, 76, 77, 78, 79, 92, 93, 126, 127, 138, 139, 142

Research: F. Corbett, S.T. Storoschuk
Design: David Shaw, Rene Zamic, and Gerry Goldberg
Cover Illustrations: Rene Zamic

Acknowledgements

This page constitutes an extension of the copyright page. Every reasonable care has been taken to trace ownership of copyright material. Information will be welcome which will enable the publisher to rectify any reference or credit.
Nine Lives © 1969, 1974 by Ursula K. Le Guin; originally appeared in *Playboy* Magazine; reprinted by permission of the author and her agent, Virginia Kidd.
Design: from *The Poetry of Robert Frost* edited by Edward Connery Lathem. Copyright 1936 by Robert Frost. Copyright © 1964 by Lesley Frost Ballantine. Copyright © 1969 by Holt, Rinehart and Winston, Inc. Reprinted by permission of Holt, Rinehart and Winston, Inc.
Fern Hill: from Dylan Thomas, *Collected Poems 1934-1952.* Reprinted by permission of J.M. Dent and Sons Ltd.
He too is vulnerable: from *Introduction to Humanistic Psychology* by Charlotte Butler and Melanie Allen. Copyright © 1972 by Wadsworth Publishing Company, Inc. Reprinted by permission of the publisher, Brooks/Cole Publishing Company, Monterey, California.
Danger: reprinted by permission of the author, Louis Dudek.
On Malay Witchcraft: from *The Book of Imaginary Beings* by Jorge Luis Borges with Margarita Guerro. Translated by Norman Thomas di Giovanni in collaboration with the author. Copyright © 1969 by Jorge Luis Borges and Norman Thomas di Giovanni. Reprinted by permission of the publishers, E.P. Dutton and Co., Inc.
The Circular Ruins: from Jorge Luis Borges, *Labyrinths.* Copyright © 1962 by New Directions Publishing Corporation. Reprinted by permission of New Directions Publishing Corporation.
The Heavy Bear Who Goes With Me: from Delmore Schwartz, *Selected Poems: Summer Knowledge.* Copyright 1938 by New Directions Publishing Corporation. Reprinted by permission of New Directions Publishing Corporation.
excerpts from *The Secret of the Golden Flower* by Richard Wilhelm: reprinted by permission of Routledge, and Kegan Paul Ltd., London.
The Dweller in Dark Valley: from Robert E. Howard, *Echoes From An Iron Harp.* Reprinted by permission of Glenn Lord.
The Magi, The Crazed Moon, The Double Vision of Michael Robartes, The Second Coming: from *Collected Poems* by W.B. Yeats. Reprinted with permission of M.B. Yeats, Miss Anne Yeats and Macmillan Co. of Canada.
The Shell: from *Collected Poems* by James Stephens. By permission of Mrs. Iris Wise; Macmillan London & Basingstoke; and the Macmillan Company of Canada Limited.

A Voyage to Arcturus: from *A Voyage to Arcturus* by David Lindsay, reprinted by permission of Macmillan Publishing Co. Inc.© Macmillan Publishing Company Inc. 1963.
Noise: reprinted from *Eight Fantasms and Magics* by Jack Vance. Copyright Jack Vance. Reprinted by permission of the author and his agents, Scott Meredith Literary Agency, Inc., 580 Fifth Avenue, New York, N.Y. 10036.
The Doors of Perception: from *The Doors of Perception* by Aldous Huxley. Copyright 1954 by Aldous Huxley. Reprinted by permission of Mrs. Laura Huxley and Chatto and Windus.
When the Waters Were Changed and The Tale of the Sands: from *Tales of the Dervishes* by Idries Shah. Reprinted by permission of the author and Jonathan Cape Ltd., London.
Cinderella: from *Radiation* (The American Poetry Series, The Ecco Press), © 1973 by Sandra McPherson.
Lines: I Praise God's Mankind in an Old Woman: reprinted by permission of Faber and Faber Ltd. from *Fridays Child* by Wilfred Watson.
Kong Lives: reprinted by permission of the author, Ralph Hunt.
On Seeing: from *Collected Poems: the Two Seasons* by Dorothy Livesay. Reprinted by permission of McGraw-Hill Ryerson Limited.
Whispers of Immortality: reprinted by permission of Faber and Faber Ltd. from *Collected Poems 1909-1962* by T.S. Eliot.
The Trap: from *The Apple Barrel: Selected Poems 1956-1963* by Jon Stallworthy. Reprinted by permission of the author and Oxford University Press.
This Is A Photograph of Me: by permission of House of Anansi Press Limited, from *The Circle Game*, Margaret Atwood © 1967.
Dream: Bluejay or Archeopteryx: from *Procedures for Underground* by Margaret Atwood, by permission of Oxford University Press.
The Anagogic Man, The Inward Angel, Storm: from Jay Macpherson, *The Boatman,* by permission of Oxford University Press.
Paranoid, Sisters, Arras: from *The Metal and the Flower* by P.K. Page, by permission of the author.
Evensong: reprinted by permission of the author, Lester del Rey, and the author's agents, Scott Meredith Literary Agency, Inc., 580 Fifth Avenue, New York, N.Y. 10036.
Antichrist as a Child: from *Poems* by James Reaney, edited by Germaine Warkentin, New Press (1972), is reprinted by permission of the author and the publisher.
The Door: from *The Second Tree From the Corner* by E.B. White. Copyright 1939 by E.B. White. Originally appeared in *The New Yorker.* By permission of Harper & Row, Publishers, Inc.

Bestiary: from *Hath Not A Jew* by A.M. Klein. By permission of Behrman House Inc.
In a Dark Time: copyright © 1960 by Beatrice Roethke, Administratrix for the Estate of Theodore Roethke, from *The Collected Poems of Theodore Roethke.* Reprinted by permission of Doubleday & Company, Inc.
Socrates in Plato's Cave, As the Crow Flies, Song in a Rainy Season, My Grandfather: The Thunderer, Perspective, Philosopher in a Landscape, The Alchemical Hill: reprinted from *Skydeck* by Stuart Mackinnon by permission of Oberon Press.
This Is a Clearing, Flower Arranger, Dwarf Trees, Waiting, All The Trees Coloured Were: reprinted from *A Choice of Dreams* by Joy Kogawa, by permission of The Canadian Publishers, McClelland and Stewart Limited.
Vancouver Lights, Man is a Snow: reprinted from *The Collected Poems of Earle Birney* by permission of The Canadian Publishers, McClelland and Stewart Limited.
The Cave: reprinted from *The Cave* by John Newlove by permission of The Canadian Publishers, McClelland and Stewart Limited.
The Man Who Was Put In A Cage: from *Man's Search For Himself* by Rollo May. By permission of W.W. Norton & Company, Inc. Copyright 1953 by W.W. Norton & Company, Inc.
Yoke and Star by Jose Marti, The Street by Octavio Paz, The Well by Luis Pales Matos: translated by Willis Knapp Jones, from *Spanish-American Literature in Translation. A Selection of Poetry, Fiction, and Drama since 1888,* edited by Willis Knapp Jones. Copyright © 1963 by Frederick Ungar Publishing Co.
The Unnamed Lake: reprinted with permission of F.R. Scott.
The Outsider: by H.P. Lovecraft from *Dunwich Horror and Others* by permission of Arkham House.
The Hounds of Tindalos: by Frank Belknap Long, by permission of Arkham House.
The World Voice and Vestigia: by Bliss Carman, from *Selected Poems,* reprinted by permission of The Canadian Publishers, McClelland and Stewart Limited.
The Cold Green Element: from *Collected Poems* by Irving Layton, reprinted by permission of The Canadian Publishers, McClelland and Stewart Limited.
Minotaur: by Michael Ayrton, *A Chamber of Horrors,* ed. John Hadfield, published by Studio Vista Ltd., Highgate Hill, London.
The Fear: by Andrew Young, from *Collected Poems,* published by Rupert Hart-Davies Ltd., London.
To End Her Fear: by John Freeman, from *Imagination,* ed. Rhodri H. Jones, published by Heinemann Educational Books Ltd., London.
A Separate Reality: by Carlos Castaneda, from *Further Conversations With Don Juan.* Copyright © 1971 Carlos Castaneda. Published by Simon and Schuster, New York.
Lirazel Blows Away: from *The King of Elfland's Daughter* by Lord Dunsany, published by Ballantine Books, New York, by permission of John Cushman Associates.
A Recognition: by Mark Rudman. First appeared in *Harper's Magazine,* January, 1970, Vol. 240, No. 1436.
Elijah Browning: by Edgar Lee Masters, from *Spoon River Anthology,* published by the Macmillan Publishing Co. Ltd., London.
Applelore: by Judy Stonehill, appeared in *Analecta Magazine* (Winter, 1968).
The Ship of Ishtar: from *The Ship of Ishtar* by A. Merritt, published by Avon Books, New York.
Hush!: by Zenna Henderson, from *Beyond Fantasy Fiction,* published by Galaxy Publishing Corp., New York.
Summer: by John Ashbery, appeared in *Harper's Magazine,* January, 1970, Vol. 240, No. 1436.
Not Ideas About the Thing but the Thing Itself: Copyright 1954 by Wallace Stevens. Reprinted from *The Collected Poems of Wallace Stevens* by permission of Alfred A. Knopf, Inc.
Reality is an Activity of the Most August Imagination: From *Opus Posthumous,* by Wallace Stevens. Copyright © 1957 by Elsie Stevens and Holly Stevens. Reprinted by permission of Alfred A. Knopf, Inc.
Connoisseur of Chaos: Copyright 1942 and renewed 1970 by Holly Stevens. Reprinted from *The Collected Poems of Wallace Stevens* by permission of Alfred A. Knopf, Inc.
Anecdote of the Jar, Tattoo: Copyright 1923 and renewed 1951 by Wallace Stevens. Reprinted from *The Collected Poems of Wallace Stevens* by permission of Alfred A. Knopf, Inc.
The God of The Labyrinth: by Colin Wilson. Published by Mayflower Books Ltd., London. Copyright © 1970 Colin Wilson. Reprinted by permission of the author's agents, Bolt and Watson.